Vocabulary WORKS

Level A

Dr. Alvin Granowsky

Copyright © 1995 by Modern Curriculum Press, Inc.

An imprint of Paramount Supplemental Education
250 James Street
Morristown, New Jersey 07960

ISBN 0-8136-1708-1

2 3 4 5 6 7 8 9 10   98 97 96

TABLE OF CONTENTS

THE SHOCKING TRUTH ABOUT EELS

The Moray is the most dangerous of all eels.

Eels are fish that look like snakes. But, unlike most fish, eels have no **fins**. They glide through the water using their muscles to push their **thin** bodies forward. Some eels live in **fresh** water. Some live in salt water. It's not easy to **measure** an eel. They can be as **short** as three inches and as **long** as six feet.

Another fish that looks like a snake is called the electric eel. It lives in muddy rivers in South America. It can shock other **animals** with electricity. An electric eel can make enough power to knock out an alligator! And here's one more shocking fact about these fish. They aren't really eels at all. They are part of the catfish family.

READERS LOOK FOR DETAILS

Where do electric eels live?

Check the best answer.

- ☐ in South America
- ☐ in North America
- ☐ in Africa
- ☐ in the ocean

ABC ORDER FOUND

Print the New Words in alphabetical order.

☞ When two words have the same first letter, use the second letter to see which word comes first.

f<u>i</u>nd comes before **f<u>r</u>ee**

New Words

short

eels

fins

fresh

thin

long

measure

animals

1. _____   5. _____

2. _____   6. _____

3. _____   7. _____

4. _____   8. _____

WORD MATCH PUTS MEANINGS IN THEIR PLACE

Use a New Word to finish each meaning. Write the words in the boxes.

1. Some fish that look like snakes are ☐☐☐ .

2. A fish swims with its ☐☐☐☐ .

3. Something that is not thick is ☐☐☐☐ .

4. Water that is not salty is ☐☐☐☐☐ .

5. A thing that is not tall is ☐☐☐☐☐ .

6. Something that extends over a distance is ☐☐☐☐ .

7. Living creatures are called ☐☐☐☐☐☐☐ .

8. "To find the size of something" means ☐☐☐☐☐☐☐ .

4

COMPLETED SENTENCES GIVE SHOCKING RESULTS

Finish these sentences. Print a New Word on each line.

1. John saw some _____ in the water.

2. They did not have any _____ .

3. We only had to wait a _____ time for the show to start.

4. It was a _____ show.

5. Compared to some people, Mary is very _____ .

6. She drinks a lot of _____ water.

7. We went to the zoo to see the _____ .

8. I had to _____ my room to see if the furniture would fit.

NEW WORDS FORM SUPER GROUPS

Some words go together in **groups**. For example, **apples**, **pears**, and **grapes** are in a group called **fruit**.

Circle the three words under each New Word that belong in the same group.

1. <u>Animals</u> with fur

   bear   dog   sheep   snake

2. Units of <u>measure</u>

   inches   vegetables   feet   meters

3. Things that have <u>fins</u>

   fish   rockets   divers   snakes

Need help?
Use the
glossary
on page 103.

DID YOU KNOW?

❖ A coral reef looks like a rocky underwater island. It is really made up of the skeletons of certain sea animals.

❖ Electric eels aren't the only sea animals that can give shocks. The electric eel's relative, the electric catfish, can also zap other animals with electricity.

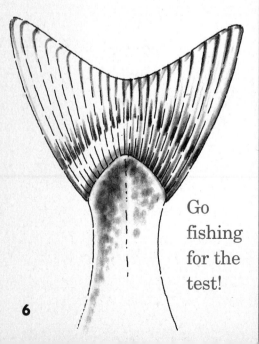

Go fishing for the test!

READ MORE ABOUT IT

- *Dangerous Fish* by Ray Broekel. (Children's Press, 1982)
- *Eyewitness: Fish* by Steve Parker. (Knopf, 1990)
- *Those Amazing Eels* by Cheryl M. Halton. (Dillon Press, 1990)
- *Think of an Eel* by Karen Wallace. (Candlewick Press, 1993)

A FISHY TALE

 Look at the picture below. These children have just bought a goldfish. Write a story about the picture.

These questions will help guide your writing:
- What will the children name their fish?
- How should they care for their fish?
- Where will they put the fish?

Use at least three New Words in your story.

SECRETS TO SUCCESS ON TESTS

Mark your answers with a sharpened, no. 2 pencil. Have several handy in case one breaks.

Look at each picture. Fill in the circle next to the word that best fits each picture.

1
- Ⓐ eels
- Ⓑ fins
- Ⓒ animals
- Ⓓ snakes

3
- Ⓐ fish
- Ⓑ fins
- Ⓒ animals
- Ⓓ eels

2
- Ⓐ fish
- Ⓑ eels
- Ⓒ animals
- Ⓓ fins

4
- Ⓐ measure
- Ⓑ glide
- Ⓒ live
- Ⓓ shock

Read each sentence. Fill in the circle next to the word that best completes the sentence.

5 He is so ____ he cannot see over the crowd.
- Ⓐ thin
- Ⓑ fresh
- Ⓒ long
- Ⓓ short

6 Eels, cats, and dogs all belong to the same group called ____ .
- Ⓐ short
- Ⓑ animals
- Ⓒ thin
- Ⓓ fish

7 Water that is low in salt is called ____ water.
- Ⓐ thin
- Ⓑ fresh
- Ⓒ short
- Ⓓ long

8 Use this ruler to find how ____ the rope is.
- Ⓐ fresh
- Ⓑ thin
- Ⓒ short
- Ⓓ open

9 The ____ body of an eel makes it look like a snake.
- Ⓐ short
- Ⓑ long
- Ⓒ flat
- Ⓓ fresh

10 Eels do not have ____ like other fish.
- Ⓐ animals
- Ⓑ fins
- Ⓒ feet
- Ⓓ electricity

RUN, DRIBBLE, JUMP, SHOOT

She can run. She can **dribble**. She can jump. She can shoot. She's got what it takes to be a **major** basketball star. Her name is Jolette Law, and she's a **member** of the famous Harlem Globetrotters.

Jolette "Jazzy" Law went to Wilson High School in Florence, South Carolina. There she was named **twice** as a National High School All-American.

Jolette went to **college** in Iowa and scored over a thousand points during her career. She was able to **accomplish** a lot.

But Jolette thinks her greatest accomplishment was being **selected** to be a Harlem Globetrotter. With her many talents, Jolette just might be the **perfect** player.

DETAILS SLAM-DUNKED

What does Jolette think her greatest accomplishment is?

Check the best answer.
_____ going to college in Iowa
_____ being a perfect player
_____ being selected to play with the Harlem Globetrotters
_____ being able to run, dribble, jump, and shoot

ORDER IN THE COURT

Print the New Words in alphabetical order.

☞ When two words have the same first letter, use the second letter to see which word comes first.

m<u>a</u>n comes before **m<u>e</u>at**

New Words

major	accomplish
member	selected
twice	dribble
college	perfect

1. _____   5. _____

2. _____   6. _____

3. _____   7. _____

4. _____   8. _____

GETTING IN SHAPE

Use a New Word to finish each meaning.
Fill in the word shapes.

1. A school for students after high school is a ⬚⬚⬚⬚⬚⬚⬚ .

2. One of a team of people is called a ⬚⬚⬚⬚⬚⬚ .

3. To be chosen from among many is to be ⬚⬚⬚⬚⬚⬚⬚⬚ .

4. "Very important" means ⬚⬚⬚⬚⬚ .

5. Someone or something that has no faults is ⬚⬚⬚⬚⬚⬚⬚ .

6. To succeed in doing something is to ⬚⬚⬚⬚⬚⬚⬚⬚⬚⬚ .

7. To bounce the ball is to ⬚⬚⬚⬚⬚⬚⬚ .

8. To do something two times is to do it ⬚⬚⬚⬚⬚ .

COMPLETING THE SENTENCES

Print the New Word that best completes each sentence.

New Words

1. I want to go to _____ when I grow up.
   major   college   Iowa

2. I have the _____ answer for all your problems.
   perfect   selected   major

3. She can _____ the ball around a player and down the floor.
   shoot   dribble   jump

4. I will _____ some important things in my life.
   college   member   accomplish

5. A _____ baseball player will visit our classroom.
   member   major   dribble

6. I have told you _____ to finish your work.
   dribble   twice   maybe

7. I _____ you because I know you will do a good job.
   selected   major   dribble

8. He is a _____ of my team.
   college   perfect   member

major

member

twice

college

selected

accomplish

dribble

perfect

SEARCHING FOR A WINNER

Circle each New Word in the word search.

```
H P E R F E C T A T L T S H M
W N S B I S O W Z B U M G D L
A C C O M P L I S H L E N F M
G V F R A Q L C Y K E M C K F
C N J M J O E E D R I B B L E
U E A K O L G N X O V E Z R B
O J C X R P E W P G D R A H F
I D S E L E C T E D J E Y Q I
```

WHO'S ON FIRST?

Jolette "Jazzy" Law is one of eight women to play with the Harlem Globetrotters. Who was the first?

Answer: Lynette Woodard joined the team in 1985. She went on to win an Olympic gold medal.

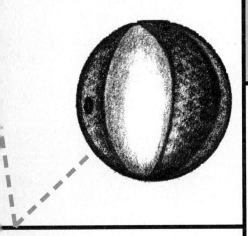

SPORT SPOT

The Guinness Book of World Records states that Pearl Moore of Francis Morton College holds the record for most points scored in basketball by a woman in a college career. Guess how many points Pearl scored.

Answer: 4,061

Shoot for the test!

LEARN MORE ABOUT BASKETBALL

READ:

- *B-Ball: The Team That Never Lost a Game* by Ron Jones. (Bantam Books, 1990)
- *Lynette Woodard* by Matthew Newman. (Crestwood House, 1986)
- *The Harlem Globetrotters: Fifty Years of Fun and Games* by Chuck Menville. (D. McKay Company, 1978)

WATCH:

- *Harlem Globetrotters: Six Decades of Magic.* (Fries Home Video, 1988)
- *Do It Better Basketball.* (ESPN Home Video, 1990)
- *Michael Jordan's Playground.* (CBS/Fox Video, 1991)

MY BASKETBALL STORY

 Write a story about this picture.

Use these questions to help you get started:
- What is happening in the picture?
- What do the girls have to do to score a basket?
- How does the other team try to stop the girls from scoring?

Use at least three of the New Words in your story.

SCORE HIGHER ON TESTS

Answer all questions of which you are sure. After you have gone through the test once, go back to the difficult questions.

Read each group of words. Fill in the circle next to the word that means the __same__ as the underlined word.

1 a <u>major</u> show
   Ⓐ funny
   Ⓑ long
   Ⓒ important
   Ⓓ short

2 <u>selected</u> for the team
   Ⓐ wanted
   Ⓑ picked
   Ⓒ made
   Ⓓ won

3 went to <u>college</u>
   Ⓐ school
   Ⓑ house
   Ⓒ store
   Ⓓ park

4 heard it <u>twice</u>
   Ⓐ three times
   Ⓑ one time
   Ⓒ two times
   Ⓓ ten times

Read each sentence. Fill in the circle next to the word that best completes the sentence.

5 Are you a ____ of that team?
   Ⓐ college
   Ⓑ accomplishment
   Ⓒ selected
   Ⓓ member

6 Watch Jolette ____ the ball down the court.
   Ⓐ jump
   Ⓑ dribble
   Ⓒ score
   Ⓓ play

7 "Jazzy" Law has so many talents, she is called a ____ player.
   Ⓐ selected
   Ⓑ member
   Ⓒ college
   Ⓓ perfect

8 She will ____ much in her life.
   Ⓐ member
   Ⓑ accomplish
   Ⓒ major
   Ⓓ perfect

9 You have been ____ to read the story.
   Ⓐ selected
   Ⓑ perfect
   Ⓒ major
   Ⓓ scored

10 My older sister goes to ____ in Iowa.
   Ⓐ championships
   Ⓑ accomplish
   Ⓒ college
   Ⓓ Harlem

STOP

TEN, NINE, EIGHT... BLASTOFF!

From inside the space **shuttle** *Endeavour*, Dr. Mae Jemison listened to the countdown. "Ten, nine, eight, seven. . . ." It was September 12, 1992, and she was about to become the first African American woman to go into outer space.

As a child, Mae liked **mathematics** and **science**. She was good at working with numbers and liked playing with the **microscope**. She dreamed of being a scientist. Mae became not only a scientist, but a **doctor** and an **astronaut**, too!

Today Mae is helping bring better **medicine** to people in western Africa. She also teaches math and science. Maybe someday one of her **students** will be an astronaut, too!

"Some people say that I don't look like an astronaut. But that's okay, because I am!"

THAT'S THE IDEA

What kind of work is Dr. Jemison doing now?

Check the best answer.

☐ She is an astronaut.

☐ She helps people learn to fly.

☐ She studies frogs in space.

☐ She teaches math and science.

ALPHABET KEEPS WORDS IN ORDER

Print the New Words in alphabetical order.

New Words

shuttle
mathematics
science
microscope
doctor
astronaut
medicine
students

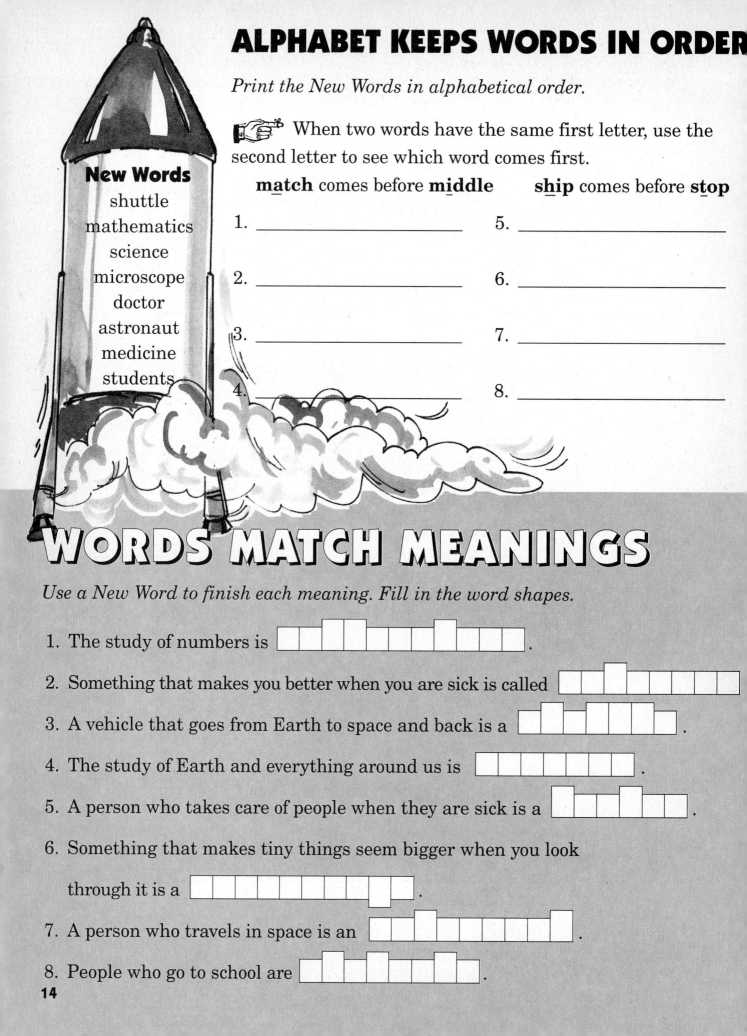

When two words have the same first letter, use the second letter to see which word comes first.

m<u></u>atch comes before **m<u></u>iddle**   **sh<u></u>ip** comes before **st<u></u>op**

1. _____   5. _____

2. _____   6. _____

3. _____   7. _____

4. _____   8. _____

WORDS MATCH MEANINGS

Use a New Word to finish each meaning. Fill in the word shapes.

1. The study of numbers is ⬚⬚⬚⬚⬚⬚⬚⬚⬚⬚⬚ .

2. Something that makes you better when you are sick is called ⬚⬚⬚⬚⬚⬚⬚⬚ .

3. A vehicle that goes from Earth to space and back is a ⬚⬚⬚⬚⬚⬚⬚ .

4. The study of Earth and everything around us is ⬚⬚⬚⬚⬚⬚⬚ .

5. A person who takes care of people when they are sick is a ⬚⬚⬚⬚⬚⬚ .

6. Something that makes tiny things seem bigger when you look

   through it is a ⬚⬚⬚⬚⬚⬚⬚⬚⬚⬚ .

7. A person who travels in space is an ⬚⬚⬚⬚⬚⬚⬚⬚⬚ .

8. People who go to school are ⬚⬚⬚⬚⬚⬚⬚⬚ .

14

WORDS COMPLETE SENTENCES

Print the New Word that best completes each sentence.

1. Dr. Jemison was an _____ .
   microscope   shuttle   astronaut

2. I took the _____ for my cold.
   doctor   medicine   shuttle

3. Look into this _____ to see the tiny cells.
   doctor   microscope   medicine

4. When I study _____ , I learn about plants and animals.
   science   mathematics   medicine

5. The _____ landed on Earth this morning.
   microscope   students   shuttle

6. My teacher loves all of her _____ .
   students   science   medicine

7. I was examined by the _____ .
   medicine   doctor   mathematics

8. When I study _____ , I learn about numbers.
   mathematics   science   medicine

SOUND ISN'T EVERYTHING

👉 **Homonyms** are words that sound alike but have different meanings and spellings.

be and **bee**   **so** and **sew**

Draw a line between each pair of homonyms.

1. deer   a. ad   5. pear   a. hear

2. hall   b. fir   6. hair   b. pair

3. fur   c. haul   7. here   c. by

4. add   d. dear   8. buy   d. hare

PACK YOUR BAGS

Mae Jemison took into space an Alvin Ailey American Dance Theater poster, a flag that had flown over the Organization of African Unity, and papers from students in the Chicago public schools. What would you take?

NOTHING TO SNEEZE AT

Mae Jemison thinks it would be fun to float through space in a clear bubble with her cat Sneeze!

EXPLORE THE WORLD! READ:

• *Astronauts* by Carol Greene. (Childrens Press, 1990)

• *I Want to be an Astronaut* by Byron Barton. (Harper Collins, 1988)

• *Mae Jemison, Astronaut* by Garnet Nelson Jackson. (Modern Curriculum Press, 1993)

• *Space Songs* by Myra Cohn Livingston. (Holiday House, 1988)

BLASTING OFF ON YOUR OWN

What if you were on the shuttle taking a trip into space? Write a report about your trip. Look for more information about space travel in the library.

These questions will help you write your report:
• What would the ride be like?
• What would you find in space?
• What would happen when you got home?

Use three of the New Words in your report.

Moon walk to the test!

TEST-DAY TIPS TOLD

If you make a mistake, completely erase the incorrect answer. Don't forget to mark the correct answer for that question.

Read each group of words. Fill in the circle next to the word or words that mean the same as the underlined word.

1 the <u>shuttle</u> took off
- Ⓐ truck
- Ⓑ space vehicle
- Ⓒ car
- Ⓓ bus

2 talked to an <u>astronaut</u>
- Ⓐ doctor
- Ⓑ teacher
- Ⓒ sports person
- Ⓓ space traveler

3 studied <u>mathematics</u>
- Ⓐ arithmetic
- Ⓑ reading
- Ⓒ science
- Ⓓ phonics

4 took my <u>medicine</u>
- Ⓐ reward
- Ⓑ drug
- Ⓒ punishment
- Ⓓ money

Read each sentence below. Fill in the circle next to the word or words that best complete each sentence.

5 A person who takes care of other people's health is a . . . .
- Ⓐ shuttle
- Ⓑ medicine
- Ⓒ doctor
- Ⓓ astronaut

6 Children and adults who go to school are . . . .
- Ⓐ astronaut
- Ⓑ students
- Ⓒ medicine
- Ⓓ mathematics

7 The subject in school in which you learn about the world around you is . . . .
- Ⓐ science
- Ⓑ mathematics
- Ⓒ medicine
- Ⓓ students

8 Something that you look through to make tiny things appear larger is a . . . .
- Ⓐ astronaut
- Ⓑ doctor
- Ⓒ medicine
- Ⓓ microscope

9 A person who travels into outer space is an . . . .
- Ⓐ doctor
- Ⓑ astronaut
- Ⓒ shuttle
- Ⓓ microscope

10 Adding numbers is part of . . . .
- Ⓐ medicine
- Ⓑ students
- Ⓒ science
- Ⓓ mathematics

SNAILS SING HAWAIIANS TO SLEEP AT NIGHT

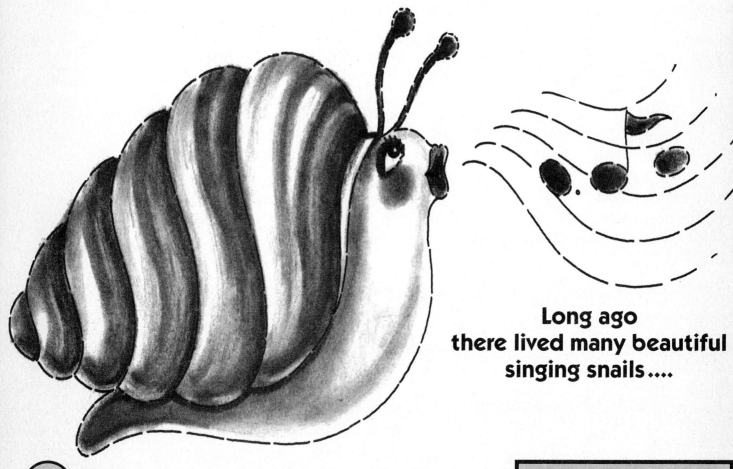

Long ago there lived many beautiful singing snails....

This isn't the **opening** of a fairy tale. Singing snails really live. They live on the **island** of Oahu in Hawaii. People say they can hear the tinkling sound of the snails' shells at night.

Hawaiians have always made up songs and hulas to **honor** singing snails. Their shells were used to make **leis**. One king even named a **valley** after the snail.

When new people came to the islands, things changed. The people brought new **crops**. They collected the snail shells and brought other animals that ate the snails.

Today **instead** of singing a happy song, the snails are in trouble. The Hawaiians are working to get the snails on the **endangered** list.

DETAIL THE SNAILS

Where do the singing snails live?

Check the best answer.

◯ in hulas and leis

◯ in Ohio

◯ in Hawaii

◯ in the ocean

THE ABC'S OF SNAILS

Print the New Words in alphabetical order.

When two words have the same first letter, use the second letter to see which word comes first.

ink comes before **is**sue

1. _____

2. _____

3. _____

4. _____

5. _____

6. _____

7. _____

8. _____

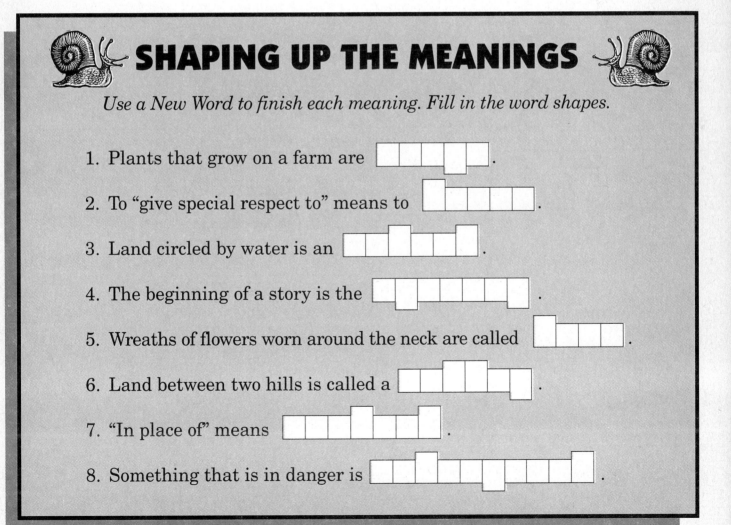

SHAPING UP THE MEANINGS

Use a New Word to finish each meaning. Fill in the word shapes.

1. Plants that grow on a farm are ⬚⬚⬚⬚⬚ .

2. To "give special respect to" means to ⬚⬚⬚⬚⬚ .

3. Land circled by water is an ⬚⬚⬚⬚⬚⬚ .

4. The beginning of a story is the ⬚⬚⬚⬚⬚⬚⬚ .

5. Wreaths of flowers worn around the neck are called ⬚⬚⬚⬚ .

6. Land between two hills is called a ⬚⬚⬚⬚⬚⬚ .

7. "In place of" means ⬚⬚⬚⬚⬚⬚⬚ .

8. Something that is in danger is ⬚⬚⬚⬚⬚⬚⬚⬚⬚⬚ .

MISSING WORDS COMPLETE SENTENCES

Print the New Word that best completes each sentence.

1. We made _____ out of flowers.
   crops   leis   island

2. I enjoyed the _____ of the story.
   opening   island   valley

3. Which presidents do we _____ in February?
   endangered   live   honor

4. Oahu is an _____ in Hawaii.
   valley   opening   island

5. The lives of the snails are _____ .
   opening   instead   endangered

6. The _____ was cooler than the hills around it
   opening   island   valley

7. I will help you _____ of going out.
   instead   leis   opening

8. We gathered the _____ from the field.
   island   crops   leis

New Words

opening

island

honor

leis

valley

crops

instead

endangered

STORY WORDS UNSCRAMBLED

Unscramble the New Words in this story and print them on the lines.

I walked through the _____ to find some flowers for our

_____ . I found many _____ growing

   ylevla

_____ . I found many _____ growing
   seil   *prcos*

_____ . The fields reminded me of the _____
   senidat   *npeigon*

of my favorite book about the _____ of Oahu. In the book, people
                               dslnai

_____ plants and animals that are _____ .
   noohr   *ganednedre*

20

DID YOU KNOW?

> The singing snail has no legs. The whole bottom of a snail's body is one smooth foot.

> Land snails, like singing snails, make their own paths. They slide forward on a slippery slime highway that oozes from their bodies. This gooey slime protects the snail's delicate body as it travels.

LAND OF PLENTY

Look at the pictures below. Think of how these pictures are alike and how they are different. Write several sentences about these places.

Use these questions to help you get started:

- How are these places alike and different?
- How would you travel to these places?
- In which of these places would you like to live?

Use three of the New Words in your writing.

MUSIC TO YOUR EARS

READ:

- *The Last Princess, the Story of Princess Ka'lulani of Hawai'i* by Fay Stanley. (Macmillan, 1991)

LISTEN:

- *Hawaiian Drum Dance Chants, Sound of Power in Time.* (Compact disk, Smithsonian/Folkways Records, 1969)

WATCH:

- *Hawaiian Paradise Lost.* (Video, BFA Educational Media, 1984)
- *Kuma Hula Keepers of Culture.* (Video, Rhapsody Films, 1990)

Don't move at a snail's pace. Hurry on to the test!

IMPROVE YOUR TEST SCORES

If you have time at the end of a test, reread the directions and test questions.

Look at each picture. Fill in the circle next to the word that best fits each picture.

1
- Ⓐ opening
- Ⓑ leis
- Ⓒ island
- Ⓓ valley

3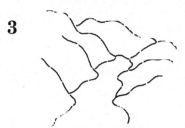
- Ⓐ leis
- Ⓑ island
- Ⓒ endangered
- Ⓓ valley

2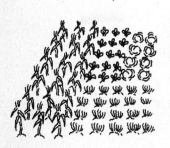
- Ⓐ valley
- Ⓑ crops
- Ⓒ island
- Ⓓ opening

4
- Ⓐ opening
- Ⓑ leis
- Ⓒ endangered
- Ⓓ crops

Read each sentence. Fill in the circle next to the word that best completes the sentence.

5 Did you like the ____ of the story?
- Ⓐ crops
- Ⓑ leis
- Ⓒ opening
- Ⓓ valley

6 Some animals on the ____ list cannot be found anymore.
- Ⓐ crops
- Ⓑ endangered
- Ⓒ opening
- Ⓓ valley

7 I will go by bus ____ of traveling by train.
- Ⓐ instead
- Ⓑ endangered
- Ⓒ honor
- Ⓓ opening

8 In February we ____ two presidents.
- Ⓐ instead
- Ⓑ endangered
- Ⓒ honor
- Ⓓ live

9 The farmer will gather the ____ next week.
- Ⓐ crops
- Ⓑ leis
- Ⓒ endangered
- Ⓓ opening

10 Because the hills were so steep, most of the people lived in the ____.
- Ⓐ crops
- Ⓑ opening
- Ⓒ valley
- Ⓓ island

THANKS, DR. SEUSS

Did you know that the *Cat in the Hat* and *Sam-I-Am* were created by the same person? Theodor Seuss Geisel, better known as Dr. Seuss, **wrote** and **illustrated** books that children have come to love.

But Dr. Seuss was not always so **adored.** Theodor's art teacher told him he couldn't draw well. But Theodor continued, and in 1937 he wrote and illustrated his first book. He sent the book to thirty places before someone would **publish** it.

Dr. Seuss said, "Writing children's books is hard **work**." He wrote and rewrote his books to get them **right**. It's not a **secret** that he thought children should have just as much fun **reading** books as grown-ups do.

GET THE DETAILS

What did Dr. Seuss start doing in 1937?

Check the best answer.
- ❏ drawing pictures
- ❏ going to school
- ❏ writing and illustrating children's books
- ❏ taking art classes

THE ABC'S OF DR. SEUSS

New Words

secret

wrote

adored

illustrated

publish

work

right

reading

Print the New Words in alphabetical order.

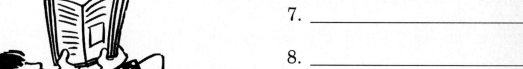 When two words have the same first letter, use the second letter to see which word comes first.

r<u>e</u>al comes before **r<u>i</u>de**

1. _____

2. _____

3. _____

4. _____

5. _____

6. _____

7. _____

8. _____

WORDS MATCH MEANINGS

Use a New Word to finish each meaning. Fill in the word shapes.

1. Something you do not tell others is a ⬚⬚⬚⬚⬚⬚ .

2. Understanding written words is called ⬚⬚⬚⬚⬚⬚⬚ .

3. "Correct" or "with no mistakes" means ⬚⬚⬚⬚⬚ .

4. "Thought very highly of" means ⬚⬚⬚⬚⬚⬚ .

5. "Drew pictures to go with" means ⬚⬚⬚⬚⬚⬚⬚⬚⬚⬚⬚ .

6. To make a book is to ⬚⬚⬚⬚⬚⬚⬚ .

7. "Told in writing" means ⬚⬚⬚⬚⬚ .

8. Something to be done, especially as part of one's job is called ⬚⬚⬚⬚ .

SENTENCE SENSE WITH SEUSS

Print the New Word that best completes each sentence.

1. I really _____ *Cat in the Hat.*
   right   work   adored

2. Dr. Seuss _____ his books himself.
   illustrated   work   reading

3. Mother _____ a note to the teacher.
   secret   wrote   reading

4. Who will _____ my new book?
   publish   wrote   right

5. This is very hard _____ .
   secret   work   publish

6. Can you keep a _____ ?
   work   right   secret

7. I hope you always do the _____ thing.
   secret   right   adored

8. My favorite time of day is when we are _____ books.
   wrote   adored   reading

COMPLETE THIS PUZZLE

Find two words in the middle of the puzzle that answer this riddle:
What do you call a soaked animal?

1. a job   ___ ___ ___ ___

2. understanding words on a page   ___ ___ ___ ___ ___ ___ ___

3. correct   ___ ___ ___ ___ ___

4. produce a book   ___ ___ ___ ___ ___ ___ ___

5. loved   ___ ___ ___ ___ ___ ___

6. put in writing   ___ ___ ___ ___ ___

FUN FACT

Dr. Seuss lived in an old lighthouse with a sign that read "Beware of the Cat."

STORIES IN PICTURES

Dr. Seuss got the idea for *Thidwick: The Big-Hearted Moose* and for *Horton Hatches the Egg* by studying doodles he had drawn while he was thinking about something else.

ANOTHER DR. SEUSS?

Dr. Seuss wrote about Mulberry Street. Write a story about the street where you live.

Use these questions to help you get started:
- What is the name of your street?
- Did anything funny happen on your street?
- What is the thing you like best about your street?

Use three of the New Words in your story.

DR. SEUSS ON THE LOOSE

READ:
- *And to Think That I Saw It on Mulberry Street* by Dr. Seuss. (Random House, 1989)
- *The 500 Hats of Bartholomew Cubbins* by Dr. Seuss. (Vanguard, 1938)
- *The Cat in the Hat* by Dr. Seuss. (Random House, 1957)

Visit your library. He's written a lot more!

Write your way to the test!

TEST-TAKING SECRETS REVEALED

Be careful of answers that look or sound alike. Say the words to yourself.

Read each group of words. Fill in the circle next to the word or words that mean the same as the underlined word.

1 <u>wrote</u> a letter
- Ⓐ used a brush to paint
- Ⓑ put words on paper
- Ⓒ took a picture of
- Ⓓ talked about

2 <u>adored</u> the dress
- Ⓐ liked very much
- Ⓑ lived for
- Ⓒ was dressed in
- Ⓓ looked like

3 <u>illustrated</u> the book
- Ⓐ wrote
- Ⓑ drew pictures for
- Ⓒ read aloud
- Ⓓ printed

4 <u>reading</u> the paper
- Ⓐ using
- Ⓑ understanding written words
- Ⓒ looking at pictures
- Ⓓ folding

5 <u>publish</u> a book
- Ⓐ print and sell
- Ⓑ read
- Ⓒ send
- Ⓓ tell about

6 kept a <u>secret</u>
- Ⓐ something well-known
- Ⓑ picture
- Ⓒ something hidden
- Ⓓ book

Read each sentence below. Fill in the circle next to the word or words that best complete each sentence.

7 Doing a job or making something is called . . . .
- Ⓐ reading
- Ⓑ work
- Ⓒ right
- Ⓓ pictures

8 Being correct is being . . . .
- Ⓐ secret
- Ⓑ loved
- Ⓒ work
- Ⓓ right

9 Something you keep to yourself is called a . . . .
- Ⓐ reading
- Ⓑ pictures
- Ⓒ secret
- Ⓓ work

10 Understanding written words is called . . . .
- Ⓐ reading
- Ⓑ work
- Ⓒ loved
- Ⓓ secret

MYSTERY VOICE IS PUZZLING

Have you ever wondered about those voices **behind** your favorite cartoons? Did you know the voice behind Scooby-Doo is actor Don Messic. **Comic** Robin Williams was the voice for the genie in the movie *Aladdin*.

The first cartoon with a speaking animal was made in 1928. In it people **heard** the voice of Walt Disney as the character Mickey Mouse.

To make a cartoon, **artists** and **writers** do their work first. They make a **script** by writing and drawing each scene of the story. Then the **music** and voices are added.

So, if you think you've heard that voice before, don't be surprised. It might belong to a movie **star** you know!

Don Messic is the voice behind all these famous cartoon characters.

WHAT'S THE BIG IDEA?

What is the main idea of this story?

Check the best answer.

❑ Robin Williams is a famous comic.

❑ The voices you hear in cartoons sometimes belong to actors you know.

❑ Walt Disney and Mickey Mouse made the first cartoon.

❑ Movie stars have very interesting voices.

ALPHABET PUTS WORDS IN ORDER

Print the New Words in alphabetical order.

☞ Look at the first letter of each New Word. When the first letters are the same, use the second letters.

s̲c̲reen comes before **s̲t̲amp**

NEW WORDS

behind
comic
heard
artists
writers
script
music
star

1. _____

2. _____

3. _____

4. _____

5. _____

6. _____

7. _____

8. _____

GET YOUR FACTS RIGHT

Use a New Word to finish each meaning. Fill in the word shapes.

1. People who put their ideas on paper are ⬚⬚⬚⬚⬚⬚⬚ .

2. A performer who tells jokes is a ⬚⬚⬚⬚⬚ .

3. People who paint pictures are ⬚⬚⬚⬚⬚⬚⬚ .

4. To be in back of something is to be ⬚⬚⬚⬚⬚⬚ .

5. A written form of a play or movie is called a ⬚⬚⬚⬚⬚⬚ .

6. Songs and tunes are ⬚⬚⬚⬚⬚ .

7. An important actor is a ⬚⬚⬚⬚ .

8. "Listened to" means ⬚⬚⬚⬚⬚ .

29

WORDS STAR IN SENTENCES

Use a New Word to finish each sentence.

New Words

behind	writers
comic	script
heard	music
artists	star

1. Do you like soft or loud _____ ?

2. The _____ are painting their pictures.

3. The _____ of the show is Mickey Mouse.

4. I left my boots _____ the door.

5. I _____ you because you were noisy.

6. The actor had to study her _____ .

7. All the first graders were _____ by the end of the year.

8. He is the funniest _____ that I know.

DID YOU KNOW?

✳ What was one of the earliest full-length cartoons? Hint: It starred some happy, sneezy, sleepy characters.

Answer: *Snow White and the Seven Dwarfs*

✳ Sometimes full-length animated movies take as long as three years to make. Thousands of drawings are used for one animated movie.

PUT TWO AND TWO TOGETHER

☞ An **analogy** shows how two words compare with each other.

mouse is to **animal** as **daffodil** is to **plant**
all is to **none** as **everywhere** is to **nowhere**

Use a New Word to finish each of these analogies.

1. <u>pictures</u> are to <u>artists</u> as <u>stories</u> are to _____

2. <u>say</u> is to <u>said</u> as <u>hear</u> is to _____

3. <u>above</u> is to <u>below</u> as <u>ahead</u> is to _____

4. <u>ball</u> is to <u>sports</u> as <u>piano</u> is to _____

HAVE YOU SEEN THIS ONE?

 Write a note to a friend about what you watch on TV.

These questions will help you get started:

- What show do you like best on TV?
- Who is the star of the show?
- Why do you like this show?

Use three of the New Words in your note. If you want, draw a picture that reminds you of the show.

LOOK BEHIND THE SCENES

READ:

- *Cartoons and Cartooning* by Harvey Weiss. (Houghton Mifflin, 1990)
- *Jim Henson: From Puppets to Muppets* by Geraldine Woods. (Dillon, 1987)
- *Walt Disney's* Snow White and the Seven Dwarfs *and the Making of the Classic Film* by Richard Hollis. (Simon and Schuster Books for Young Readers, 1987)
- *Bill Peet: An Autobiography*. (Houghton Mifflin, 1989)

WATCH:

- *Beauty and the Beast*. (MAC CD-ROM from New Media Schoolhouse)
- *Snow White and the Seven Dwarfs* and *Steamboat Willie*. (Walt Disney Films)

Speak up for the test!

SECRETS TO SUCCESS ON TESTS

 Look over the entire test before you begin to see what you will be doing.

Read each group of words. Fill in the circle next to the word or words that means the __same__ as the underlined word.

1 __behind__ the box
- Ⓐ underneath
- Ⓑ in front of
- Ⓒ in back of
- Ⓓ over

2 read the __script__
- Ⓐ joke
- Ⓑ letter
- Ⓒ play
- Ⓓ picture

3 my favorite __comic__
- Ⓐ performer
- Ⓑ shoes
- Ⓒ game
- Ⓓ a kind of boat

4 __heard__ the noise
- Ⓐ saw
- Ⓑ listened to
- Ⓒ made
- Ⓓ watched for

5 a movie __star__
- Ⓐ starter
- Ⓑ beginner
- Ⓒ sky
- Ⓓ actor

6 several __writers__
- Ⓐ workers
- Ⓑ artists
- Ⓒ authors
- Ⓓ teachers

Read each sentence. Fill in the circle next to the word that best completes the sentence.

7 To listen to singing and a band playing is to listen to . . . .
- Ⓐ teachers
- Ⓑ parents
- Ⓒ music
- Ⓓ talking

8 People who paint and draw are called . . . .
- Ⓐ writers
- Ⓑ artists
- Ⓒ teachers
- Ⓓ thinkers

9 A performer who tells jokes is a . . . .
- Ⓐ comic
- Ⓑ star
- Ⓒ voice
- Ⓓ script

10 People who make up stories are called . . . .
- Ⓐ artists
- Ⓑ voices
- Ⓒ cartoons
- Ⓓ writers

CHILDREN SQUEAL WITH DELIGHT OVER THIS PERFECT PET

Are you going "hog wild" over this popular **pet**? It's not a dog or a cat. It's a pot-bellied pig.

Pot-bellied pigs are new to us. But they have been around since people lived in **caves** thousands of years ago. A book was even **written** about these pigs way back in 3486 B.C.

Pot-bellied pigs are easy to train and are very **clean**. They don't need to roll in the mud and get dirty. They only do that to keep **cool**. They prefer a shallow **pool** of clean water to cool off in.

So the next time you are **looking** for the perfect pet to **care** for, think about the pot-bellied pig.

YOU'VE GOT THE IDEA!

What is this story mainly about?

Check the best answer.

❑ people living in caves

❑ pot-bellied pigs as pets

❑ pets as good friends

❑ books about pigs

New Words
- pet
- caves
- written
- clean
- care
- pool
- cool
- looking

BRING ORDER TO THESE "HOG-WILD" WORDS

Print the New Words in alphabetical order.

☞ When two words have the same first letter, use the second letter to see which word comes first.

class comes before **co**ld   **pe**n comes before **po**t

When the first two letters are the same, use the third letters.

cart comes before **cav**ern

1. _____   5. _____

2. _____   6. _____

3. _____   7. _____

4. _____   8. _____

WORDS MATCH MEANINGS

Use a New Word to finish each meaning. Fill in the word shapes.

1. "Not dirty" means ☐☐☐☐☐ .

2. An animal that is kept at home is called a ☐☐☐ .

3. "Openings in the side of a hill or beneath the ground" means ☐☐☐☐☐ .

4. "Put in writing" means ☐☐☐☐☐☐☐ .

5. "Searching" means ☐☐☐☐☐☐☐ .

6. Not warm but not very cold is ☐☐☐☐ .

7. "To pay attention to another's needs" means to ☐☐☐☐ .

8. A puddle of water is called a ☐☐☐☐ .

FINISHING OFF THE SENTENCES

Print the New Word that best completes each sentence.

1. I have _____ a letter to the president.
   written   clean   care

2. My _____ is glad to see me when I come home.
   caves   pet   pool

3. He is _____ for a book on pigs.
   looking   written   clean

4. She is sitting in the _____ shade under the tree.
   caves   pool   cool

5. Pigs are _____ animals.
   clean   cool   pet

6. I do _____ how you feel.
   clean   care   looking

7. I don't like walking into _____ .
   clean   caves   pool

8. There is a _____ of water under the sink.
   caves   cool   pool

A PUZZLING PIG PUZZLE

Use the New Words to complete the crossword puzzle.

NEW WORDS

pet

caves

written

clean

care

pool

cool

looking

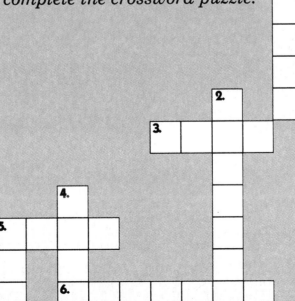

ACROSS

1. free from dirt
3. watch over
5. puddle
6. seeing

DOWN

1. holes in the earth
2. put in writing
4. not warm
5. animal

DID YOU KNOW?

- Hogs have poor eyesight but a keen sense of smell.
- Hogs are among the most intelligent animals that have been kept by people as pets.

RHYME TIME

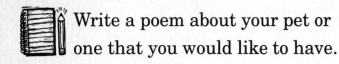 Write a poem about your pet or one that you would like to have.

Use these questions to help you get started:
- What is your pet's name?
- What tricks does your pet do?
- What do you like best about your pet?

Use three of the New Words in your poem.

Oink! Oink! Time for the test!

HOGGING THE LIMELIGHT

READ:

- *Charlotte's Web* by E. B. White. (Harper, 1952)
- *Arthur for the Very First Time* by Patricia MacLachlan. (Harper and Row, 1980)
- *The Book of Pigerics: Pig Limericks* by Arnold Lobel. (Harper and Row, 1983)
- *Julius* by Angela Johnson. (Orchard Books, 1993)

WATCH:

- *Animal Farm*. (Vestron Video)

TEST-TAKING SECRETS REVEALED

When you are asked to fill in a blank in a sentence, read the entire sentence first. Then try each of the possible answers to see which one is best.

Look at each picture. Fill in the circle next to the word that best fits each picture.

1
- Ⓐ cool
- Ⓑ pet
- Ⓒ written
- Ⓓ care

3
- Ⓐ caves
- Ⓑ cool
- Ⓒ pool
- Ⓓ pet

2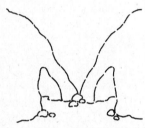
- Ⓐ pet
- Ⓑ pool
- Ⓒ caves
- Ⓓ care

4
- Ⓐ caves
- Ⓑ written
- Ⓒ cool
- Ⓓ care

Read each sentence. Fill in the circle next to the word or words that best complete the sentence.

5 It is important to ____ for a pet.
- Ⓐ cool
- Ⓑ care
- Ⓒ looking
- Ⓓ clean

6 The frog jumped into the ____ of water.
- Ⓐ caves
- Ⓑ pool
- Ⓒ friends
- Ⓓ mud

7 I am ____ for my coat.
- Ⓐ written
- Ⓑ cool
- Ⓒ clean
- Ⓓ looking

8 My mom asked us to keep our rooms ____.
- Ⓐ pet
- Ⓑ cool
- Ⓒ clean
- Ⓓ pool

9 I would like to have a ____ of my very own.
- Ⓐ cool
- Ⓑ caves
- Ⓒ care
- Ⓓ pet

10 She has ____ a book about her childhood.
- Ⓐ loved
- Ⓑ written
- Ⓒ looking
- Ⓓ clean

SCIENTISTS STUDY ROCKS TO "SAVE FACE!"

In the Black Hills of South Dakota is a world-famous **sight.** Over fifty years ago, **artist** Gutzon Borglum **carved** the heads of four United States presidents into Mount Rushmore. The heads of Washington, Jefferson, Lincoln, and Theodore Roosevelt are each carved in granite. People from all over the world come to see the **giant sculpture**. But over the years, wind, rain, and snow have made hundreds of **cracks** in the presidents' faces.

Tim Vogt studies rocks. He and other scientists take pictures of Mount Rushmore. Then they make a **map** showing the cracks. By studying the map, the scientists can see how to **fix** the cracks. With Tim's help people will enjoy Mount Rushmore for many years to come.

CHOOSE A TITLE

Which of these would be a good title for this story?

Check the best title.

- ☐ "People Enjoy Mount Rushmore"
- ☐ "Artist Carves Heads in Mountain"
- ☐ "A Visit to South Dakota"
- ☐ "Saving Mount Rushmore"

ALPHABET PUTS WORDS IN ORDER

New Words

sight
artist
carved
giant
sculpture
cracks
map
fix

Print the New Words in alphabetical order.

👉 When two words have the same first letter, use the second letter to see which word comes first.

scuff comes before **si**nce
cash comes before **cr**awl

1. _____

2. _____

3. _____

4. _____

5. _____

6. _____

7. _____

8. _____

WORDS MAKE MEANINGS

Use a New Word to finish each meaning. Fill in the word shapes.

1. "Very large" means ⬜⬜⬜⬜⬜ .

2. Something you see is a ⬜⬜⬜⬜⬜ .

3. A person who paints, draws, or carves figures is an ⬜⬜⬜⬜⬜⬜ .

4. A drawing of all or part of the Earth's surface is a ⬜⬜⬜ .

5. Breaks or openings in a surface are called ⬜⬜⬜⬜⬜⬜ .

6. Something carved or molded is a ⬜⬜⬜⬜⬜⬜⬜⬜⬜ .

7. "To repair" means to ⬜⬜⬜ .

8. "Cut or chipped to form something" means ⬜⬜⬜⬜⬜⬜ .

WORDS COMPLETE SENTENCES

Print the New Word that best completes each sentence.

New Words

sight

artist

carved

giant

sculpture

cracks

map

fix

1. I filled the _____ with cement.

2. The _____ painted a beautiful picture.

3. He _____ a figure from a piece of wood.

4. This _____ is carved from stone.

5. Can you find the town on the _____ ?

6. I saw the _____ faces on Mount Rushmore.

7. What a _____ that is!

8. Can you _____ my bike?

ANTONYMS ARE OPPOSITES

☞ **Antonyms** are words that have opposite meanings.

on and **off**

open and **closed**

Fill in the boxes with an antonym from the Word List.

Word List

giant

big

cold

winter

same

go

1. tiny ☐☐☐☐☐

2. little ☐☐☐

3. hot ☐☐☐☐

4. summer ☐☐☐☐☐☐

5. opposite ☐☐☐☐

6. come ☐☐

A DIFFERENT MOUNT RUSHMORE

People originally wanted the faces of heroes of the West, such as Buffalo Bill Cody, carved into Mount Rushmore instead of presidents.

THE UNFINISHED SCULPTURE

Mount Rushmore was never really finished in the eyes of the artist who created it. Sculptor Gutzon Borglum had wanted to carve the presidents down to their waists.

THE NEW FACE ON MOUNT RUSHMORE

Imagine that you are an artist. You are going to carve a new face in Mount Rushmore to go with the others that are already there. Write about the face you will carve.

Use these questions to help give you ideas:
* Whose face will you carve?
* Why do you think this face should be on Mount Rushmore?
* What will people say when they see the new face?

Use three of the New Words in your writing.

LEARN MORE ABOUT MOUNT RUSHMORE

BOOKS:
* *The Mount Rushmore Story* by Judith St. George. (Putnam, 1985)
* *The Story of Mount Rushmore* by Marilyn Prolman. (Children's Press, 1969)

VIDEO RECORDING:
* *Mount Rushmore and Olympic: Great National Parks.* (International Video Network, 1992)

MAGAZINE ARTICLE:
* "Mount Rushmore Turns 50" by Norman Sklarewitz. (*Boys' Life*, June, 1991)

Time to face the test!

TEST-DAY TIPS TOLD

 Be sure to erase any pencil marks that you made outside the answer circle.

Look at each picture. Fill in the circle next to the word that best fits each picture.

1
- Ⓐ map
- Ⓑ sculpture
- Ⓒ giant
- Ⓓ sight

3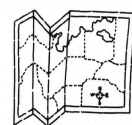
- Ⓐ map
- Ⓑ artist
- Ⓒ cracks
- Ⓓ sight

2
- Ⓐ sculpture
- Ⓑ artist
- Ⓒ cracks
- Ⓓ giant

4
- Ⓐ cracks
- Ⓑ map
- Ⓒ sculpture
- Ⓓ artist

Read each sentence below. Fill in the circle next to the word that best completes each sentence.

5 My father caught a ____ fish.
- Ⓐ giant
- Ⓑ sculpture
- Ⓒ carved
- Ⓓ map

6 I will never forget the ____ of you falling into the water.
- Ⓐ map
- Ⓑ sculpture
- Ⓒ giant
- Ⓓ sight

7 We had to stop to ____ the flat tire.
- Ⓐ map
- Ⓑ fix
- Ⓒ giant
- Ⓓ sculpture

8 He ____ the heads of the presidents out of stone.
- Ⓐ cracks
- Ⓑ fed
- Ⓒ carved
- Ⓓ fix

9 There are two ____ in that window.
- Ⓐ sight
- Ⓑ cracks
- Ⓒ map
- Ⓓ artist

10 The faces on Mount Rushmore are a large ____ .
- Ⓐ giant
- Ⓑ map
- Ⓒ artist
- Ⓓ sculpture

VISITORS FROM OUTER SPACE COME TO EARTH

Did you know we have **visitors** from outer space? The visitors come every **night**. When we see a **light** in the **sky** falling to Earth, we say, "Look, a shooting star!"

But shooting stars aren't stars at all. They are small pieces of **stone**, **rock**, and even **dust**. When these pieces hit the air, they rub against it as they fall. This makes the shooting star so hot that it lights up the night sky.

So when the sky gets **dark** on a warm, clear night, lie on your back and look for these visitors from outer space. With luck, you may see as many as four or five shooting stars every hour!

"Twinkle, twinkle, shooting star, Stone or rock is what you are!"

QUESTIONS ANSWERED ABOUT SPACE VISITORS

Are the following statements true?

Circle <u>yes</u> or <u>no</u>.

1. The visitors from outer space come in a spaceship.

   yes   no

2. The visitors from outer space are shooting stars.

   yes   no

3. Shooting stars are pieces of spaceships.

   yes   no

4. Shooting stars can be made of stone, rock, or dust.

   yes   no

BE A STAR WITH THE ALPHABET

Print the New Words in alphabetical order.

 When two words have the same first letter, use the second letter to see which word comes first.

d<u>a</u>d comes before **d<u>u</u>mp**

New Words

dust

visitors

dark

sky

light

stone

night

rock

1. _____

2. _____

3. _____

4. _____

5. _____

6. _____

7. _____

8. _____

WORDS AND MEANINGS — A MATCH MADE IN HEAVEN

Use a New Word to finish each meaning. Write the words in the boxes.

1. People who come to visit are ⬜⬜⬜⬜⬜⬜⬜⬜ .

2. When it is not day, it is ⬜⬜⬜⬜⬜ .

3. The sun shines in the ⬜⬜⬜ .

4. A small piece of hard mineral is a ⬜⬜⬜⬜ .

5. All stars give off ⬜⬜⬜⬜⬜ .

6. A large piece of stone is a ⬜⬜⬜⬜ .

7. "Fine powder" means ⬜⬜⬜⬜ .

8. When it is not light, it is ⬜⬜⬜⬜ .

MISSING WORDS FALL TO EARTH

Finish these sentences. Print a New Word on each line.

1. We are expecting _____ today.

2. The stars come out at _____ .

3. I like to watch planes fly in the _____ .

4. If you can't see, turn on the _____ .

5. I threw a small _____ across the pond.

6. Don't try to lift that heavy _____ .

7. The furniture is covered with _____ .

8. At night the sky is _____ .

SIMILIAR WORDS GROUP TOGETHER

IS THE SKY FALLING?

Some scientists think that 100 tons of shooting stars fall on Earth every day!

Circle the three words under each New Word that belong in the same group.

1. things made of <u>stone</u>

   statue   building   wall   tree

2. things in the <u>sky</u>

   house   sun   moon   airplane

3. things that give <u>light</u>

   sun   rock   lamp   fire

FIND OUT MORE ABOUT THE SPACE VISITORS

BOOKS TO READ:

- *Comets and Meteors: Visitors from Space* by Jeanne Bendick. (Millbrook Press, 1991)
- *Shooting Stars* by Franklyn M. Branley. (Crowell, 1989)
- *Sky Dragons and Flaming Swords* by Marietta Moskin. (Walker, 1985)
- *Voyagers from Space: Meteors and Meteorites* by Patricia Bauber. (Crowell, 1989)

FILMS TO VIEW:

- *Exploring Our Solar System.* (NGS Films, 1990)

CATCH A FALLING STAR

A shooting star could fall on you without your knowing it, because most are little more than bits of dust.

REPORT SHEDS LIGHT ON MOON

 Write a report about the moon. Pretend your report will be in the school newspaper. Use an encyclopedia or other books for information.

These questions will help guide your writing:
- How big is the moon?
- How far away is the moon?
- Who was the first person to walk on the moon?

Use at least three New Words in your report.

DAY AND NIGHT

We can't see shooting stars during the day because the sky is light.

Shoot over to the test!

SCORE HIGHER ON TESTS

On test day, bring your own eraser and make sure it erases cleanly.

Read each group of words. Fill in the circle next to the word that means the <u>same</u> as the underlined word.

1 <u>visitors</u> came

   Ⓐ visions

   Ⓑ guests

   Ⓒ robbers

   Ⓓ falling rock

2 <u>dust</u> on the table

   Ⓐ stars

   Ⓑ space

   Ⓒ dirt

   Ⓓ light

3 a <u>dark</u> room

   Ⓐ bright

   Ⓑ empty

   Ⓒ having no noise

   Ⓓ having no light

4 a <u>light</u> in the window

   Ⓐ brightness

   Ⓑ star

   Ⓒ shade

   Ⓓ TV

Read each sentence. Fill in the circle next to the word that best completes the sentence.

5 The ____ was filled with clouds.

   Ⓐ visitors

   Ⓑ night

   Ⓒ sky

   Ⓓ stone

6 I go to bed every ____ about 9 o'clock.

   Ⓐ nickel

   Ⓑ nine

   Ⓒ night

   Ⓓ ninja

7 I sat on the big ____ watching the birds.

   Ⓐ sky

   Ⓑ light

   Ⓒ rock

   Ⓓ dust

8 We met the ____ who came to see us.

   Ⓐ visitors

   Ⓑ stone

   Ⓒ sky

   Ⓓ night

9 Shooting stars are made of ____ .

   Ⓐ sky

   Ⓑ light

   Ⓒ night

   Ⓓ stone

10 Please clean the ____ off the desk.

   Ⓐ sky

   Ⓑ light

   Ⓒ stone

   Ⓓ dust

STOP

COCOON HIDES INCREDIBLE CHANGE!

CATERPILLAR SPROUTS WINGS, FLIES AWAY

The **butterfly** begins life as a little egg. The egg **becomes** a **worm**. This worm is called a **caterpillar**. The little caterpillar eats leaves. It gets bigger. Then it **hangs** upside down and makes a tent over itself. The tent is a **cocoon**. In the cocoon the caterpillar **changes**. After some time, the change is finished. Out comes a butterfly! Its pretty wings are wet. Soon its wings dry. The butterfly can now fly away.

A butterfly never grows. It is all **grown** when it comes out of its cocoon. One day the butterfly lays its eggs. Now its work is done. Its eggs will become butterflies someday.

CAUSE BELIEVED HIDDEN IN STORY

Why doesn't the butterfly fly away as soon as it leaves the cocoon?

Check the best answer.

◯ Its wings will not work yet.
◯ It has no place to go.
◯ It must grow first.
◯ It must lay eggs before it can fly.

ALPHA-BUTTERFLIES

Print the New Words on the lines in ABC order.

☞ Look at the first letter of each New Word. When the first letters are the same, look at the second letters.

c<u>a</u>t comes before **c<u>o</u>t**

cocoon	butterfly
becomes	hangs
changes	caterpillar
grown	worm

1. _____   5. _____

2. _____   6. _____

3. _____   7. _____

4. _____   8. _____

"I can hang like a cocoon!"

MEANING GIVES WORDS WINGS

Use a New Word to finish each meaning. Fill in the word shapes.

1. A pretty insect with wings is a ☐☐☐☐☐☐☐☐☐ .

2. A long, thin, crawling animal is a ☐☐☐☐ .

3. A worm that later becomes a butterfly is a ☐☐☐☐☐☐☐☐☐☐☐ .

4. Where a caterpillar turns into a butterfly is a ☐☐☐☐☐☐ .

5. "Turns into something else or replaces" means ☐☐☐☐☐☐☐ .

6. "Sags down or droops" means ☐☐☐☐☐ .

7. "Finished getting big" means ☐☐☐☐☐ .

8. "Comes to be" means ☐☐☐☐☐☐☐ .

SENTENCES SPROUT NEW WORDS
AMAZING CHANGE TAKES PLACE!

Finish the sentences. Print the New Words on the lines.

1. A caterpillar looks like a _____.

2. Katie saw a _____ fly by.

3. It was no longer a crawling _____.

4. It had left its _____.

5. We will not ride the pony until it is

   fully _____.

6. The picture _____ from a nail in the wall.

7. Shana _____ her clothes after school.

8. My sister _____ very silly when she

   is tired.

New Words

grown	butterfly
changes	caterpillar
becomes	cocoon
hangs	worm

WORDS TAKE FLIGHT AFTER MIX-UP

Unscramble the mixed-up words. Print the unscrambled words on the lines.

1. aleapilrrtc _____

2. mrow _____

3. lettuybfr _____

4. shnag _____

5. nooocc _____

6. ognwr _____

7. mbocsee _____

8. hasegnc _____

STRANGE NEW WORLD FOUND
DISCOVERY ANSWERS QUESTIONS

Think of what it would be like to live in a strange, new world. Make up a story about this planet.

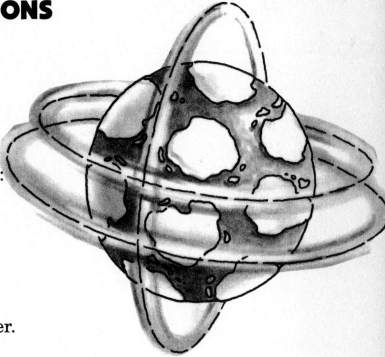

These questions will help you get started:
- How would you get there?
- What would the place look like?
- What types of people, plants, animals, and buildings would be there?

Write your story on another sheet of paper. Use at least three New Words.

BUTTERFLIES REALLY GET AROUND
There are butterflies on every continent except Antarctica. They've even been seen at the North Pole!

Worm your way to the test!

IMPROVE YOUR SCORE

 Fill in the whole answer circle, but do not spend too much time on each one.

Look at each picture. Fill in the circle next to the word that best fits the picture.

1
  Ⓐ grown
  Ⓑ cocoa
  Ⓒ butterfly
  Ⓓ cocoon

3
  Ⓐ bottom
  Ⓑ butterfly
  Ⓒ fly
  Ⓓ cocoon

2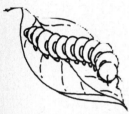
  Ⓐ caterpillar
  Ⓑ cocoon
  Ⓒ grown
  Ⓓ butterfly

4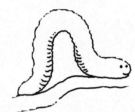
  Ⓐ warn
  Ⓑ warm
  Ⓒ worm
  Ⓓ want

Read each group of words. Fill in the circle next to the word or words that mean the <u>same</u> *as the underlined word.*

5 <u>changes</u> to water
  Ⓐ runs
  Ⓑ turns
  Ⓒ drinks
  Ⓓ adds

7 <u>becomes</u> sad
  Ⓐ gets
  Ⓑ begins
  Ⓒ hangs
  Ⓓ flies

9 hid in a <u>cocoon</u>
  Ⓐ spun case
  Ⓑ large box
  Ⓒ cup
  Ⓓ room

6 <u>hangs</u> from the hook
  Ⓐ changes
  Ⓑ lifts
  Ⓒ droops
  Ⓓ turns

8 is fully <u>grown</u>
  Ⓐ done
  Ⓑ older
  Ⓒ changed
  Ⓓ new

10 beautiful <u>butterfly</u>
  Ⓐ caterpillar
  Ⓑ warm
  Ⓒ cocoon
  Ⓓ adult caterpillar

CROSS WHEN GREEN... NOT IN BETWEEN!

What would life be like if we could not control **traffic**? How would drivers know when to stop or go? Many **streets** were not **safe** until Garrett Morgan **invented** the traffic signal.

Garrett was always **curious**. He wanted to know how things worked. He also liked to solve **problems**. He made hoods that let firefighters **breathe** clean air instead of smoke. The hoods helped save many lives.

In 1923, Garrett saw a car and a wagon hit each other on a busy street. It gave him an **idea**. He invented a way for drivers to know when to stop and go. Now green means "go" and red means "stop," and our streets are much safer.

FIRST THINGS FIRST

What happened first in Garrett Morgan's life?

Check the best answer.

◯ He invented the traffic light.
◯ He was a curious boy.
◯ He helped firefighters.
◯ He grew up.

ALPHABET KEEPS WORDS IN ORDER

traffic

safe

streets

invented

curious

problems

breathe

idea

Print the New Words in alphabetical order.

☞ When two words have the same first letter, use the second letter to see which word comes first.

sa**le** comes before **st**and

idle comes before **in**ch

1. _____

2. _____

3. _____   6. _____

4. _____   7. _____

5. _____   8. _____

WORDS AND MEANINGS TAKE SHAPE

Use a New Word to finish each meaning.
Fill in the word shapes.

1. To take air in and out of your body is to ⬚⬚⬚⬚⬚⬚⬚ .

2. "Made something new" means ⬚⬚⬚⬚⬚⬚⬚⬚ .

3. Cars and trucks on a road make up the ⬚⬚⬚⬚⬚⬚⬚ .

4. Something you think of is called an ⬚⬚⬚⬚ .

5. Pavement where cars drive are ⬚⬚⬚⬚⬚⬚⬚ .

6. "Wanting very much to learn" means ⬚⬚⬚⬚⬚⬚⬚ .

7. Things that are troublesome or are hard
   to understand are ⬚⬚⬚⬚⬚⬚⬚⬚ .

8. "Free from danger" means ⬚⬚⬚⬚ .

WORDS FILL IN SENTENCE HOLES

Print the New Word that best completes each sentence.

1. I feel _____ as long as you are with me.

2. She was _____ about what was in the package.

3. It is hard to _____ in this stuffy room.

4. He _____ a machine that would save the company time.

5. The _____ were crowded with cars and trucks.

6. Your _____ will soon be solved.

7. The _____ was backed up for miles.

8. She has no _____ how to drive a car.

ANTONYMS ARE OPPOSITES

 Antonyms are words that have opposite meanings.

big and **little**
open and **closed**

1. break	a. cool	6. right	a. under
2. dark	b. dangerous	7. over	b. light
3. warm	c. below	8. bring	c. left
4. safe	d. fix	9. heavy	d. stand
5. above	e. light	10. sit	e. take

WHO INVENTED...

Who invented some of the things we use every day? J. L. Love invented the pencil sharpener. Jan Matzeliger made

a machine to sew shoes. And Sarah Boone invented the first folding ironing board.

TAKE YOUR TURN

 Write a paragraph about how the traffic light is helpful in this picture.

Use these questions to help you get started:
- What would this intersection be like if there were no traffic light?
- How does the traffic light help the people in the cars?
- What does the traffic light tell people who are walking?

Use three of the New Words in your writing.

56 Stop for the test!

GARRETT TO THE RESCUE!

In 1916, gas exploded in a Cleveland tunnel and trapped workers inside. Wearing the hoods he invented, Garrett Morgan and his brother Frank went into the smoky tunnel and saved the lives of 32 people!

DON'T STOP FOR LONG! READ:
- *Garrett Morgan, Inventor* by Garnet Nelson Jackson. (Modern Curriculum Press, 1993)
- *I Read Signs* by Tana Hoban. (Greenwillow, 1983)
- *Outward Dreams: Black Inventors and Their Inventions* by Jim Haskins. (Walker and Company, 1991)
- *Red Light, Green Light* by Margaret Wise Brown. (Scholastic, 1992)

SECRETS TO SUCCESS ON TESTS

Look for hints in the sentence to help you understand the meaning of a word.

Read each sentence below. Fill in the circle next to the word or words that mean the _same_ as the underlined word.

1 To <u>breathe</u> is to—
Ⓐ draw something
Ⓑ swallow something
Ⓒ take air in and out
Ⓓ make something

2 To solve <u>problems</u> is to take care of—
Ⓐ your clothes
Ⓑ your books
Ⓒ things that are pretty
Ⓓ things that are causing trouble

3 To have an <u>idea</u> is to have—
Ⓐ a thought in your mind
Ⓑ a meal
Ⓒ a family
Ⓓ a picture of yourself

4 To be in <u>traffic</u> is to be —
Ⓐ in the house
Ⓑ on the road
Ⓒ at school
Ⓓ in a parking lot

Read each sentence. Fill in the circle next to the word that best completes the sentence.

5 I am ____ about what you are thinking.
Ⓐ curious   Ⓒ safe
Ⓑ invented   Ⓓ traffic

6 The ____ were empty so early in the morning.
Ⓐ problems   Ⓒ streets
Ⓑ idea   Ⓓ invented

7 Garrett Morgan ____ things that make life better for people.
Ⓐ breathe   Ⓒ traffic
Ⓑ invented   Ⓓ grew

8 You are ____ when you cross with the light.
Ⓐ invented   Ⓒ safe
Ⓑ traffic   Ⓓ curious

9 Your ____ about what to do is a good one.
Ⓐ problems   Ⓒ street
Ⓑ idea   Ⓓ traffic

10 We can take care of your ____ together.
Ⓐ street   Ⓒ problems
Ⓑ idea   Ⓓ traffic

BORING TOWN IS A BIG HIT

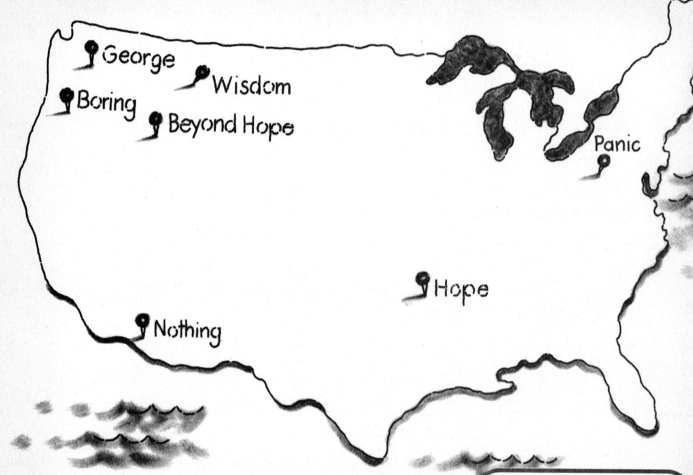

Many towns across the United States have **strange** names. **Some** people live in a **town** that is **always** boring. That's **because** they live in Boring, Oregon. In one Arkansas town, everyone lives in Hope. That's right. The town is named Hope. Hope is located **far** away from Beyond Hope, which is in Idaho.

There are many places named after the first president. But only one place **includes** both his first and last name. That place is George, Washington.

Other towns have unusual names, too. Would you want to live in Panic, Pennsylvania? It **might** be scary! But living in Wisdom, Montana, might make you feel smarter.

NAME THE MAIN IDEA

What is the main idea of the story?

Check the best answer.

___ Hope is a town in Arkansas.

___ Some towns have strange names.

___ Oregon is boring.

___ People from Montana are smart.

ALPHABET PUTS WORDS IN ORDER

New Words

strange
always
includes
because
town
some
far
might

Print the New Words in alphabetical order.

1. _____   5. _____

2. _____   6. _____

3. _____   7. _____

4. _____   8. _____

THERE'S HOPE THAT WORDS MATCH MEANINGS

Use a New Word to finish each meaning. Write the words in the boxes.

1. "A certain number of" means ☐☐☐☐ .

2. "All the time" means ☐☐☐☐☐☐ .

3. "For the reason that" means ☐☐☐☐☐☐☐ .

4. A small city is a ☐☐☐☐ .

5. Something that is not near is ☐☐☐ .

6. "Contains in a group" means ☐☐☐☐☐☐☐☐ .

7. Something that is unusual is ☐☐☐☐☐☐☐ .

8. "May possibly" means ☐☐☐☐☐ .

DID YOU KNOW?

The map of the world in your classroom probably shows the United States right in the middle. But a student in France sees France in the middle. In China, students see China in the middle of their world maps.

THERE'S HOPE FOR INCOMPLETE SENTENCES

Finish these sentences. Print a New Word on each line.

1. I only ate _____ popcorn.

2. She _____ brushes her teeth before bed.

3. I like to ride my bike _____ it is fun.

4. My friend lives in a small _____ .

5. Her house is _____ away from the store.

6. My coin collection _____ many pennies.

7. Something _____ happened last night.

8. I _____ learn to swim this summer.

READ MORE ABOUT IT

- *Children's Atlas of the United States.* (Rand McNally, 1989)
- *Town and Country* by Christopher McHugh. (Thomson Learning, 1993)
- *Cities and Citizens* by Fiona Macdonald. (Franklin Watts, 1992)

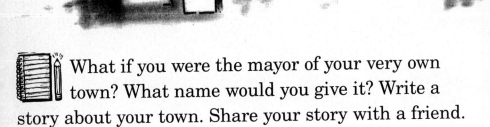

NEW TOWN NEEDS NAME

What if you were the mayor of your very own town? What name would you give it? Write a story about your town. Share your story with a friend.

These questions will help guide your writing:
• Where is your town?
• What does it look like?
• Who lives there?

Use at least three New Words in your story.

New Words

some

always

because

town

far

includes

strange

might

PUZZLE MYSTERY SOLVED

Use New Words to finish the crossword puzzle.

ACROSS

1. may possibly
4. not all
5. all the time
7. for the reason that

DOWN

2. contains in a group
3. a small city
4. unusual
6. not near

SOME PLACES AROUND THE WORLD HAVE NAMES THAT ARE EASY TO SPELL

The names of some places around the world are very easy to spell. There's a river named *O* in Holland. In Sweden, there's a town called *A*. And in China, there's a city named *U*.

Don't panic. It's test time!

SECRETS TO SUCCESS ON TESTS

Relax! If you are nervous, take a few deep breaths before you begin.

Read each group of words. Fill in the circle next to the word or words that mean the same as the underlined word.

1 <u>far</u> from here
- Ⓐ not there
- Ⓑ close to
- Ⓒ not much
- Ⓓ not near

2 <u>some</u> people
- Ⓐ one
- Ⓑ almost all
- Ⓒ a number of
- Ⓓ all

3 <u>includes</u> a reward
- Ⓐ leaves out
- Ⓑ contains
- Ⓒ adds
- Ⓓ makes

4 it <u>might</u> be
- Ⓐ always may
- Ⓑ perhaps may
- Ⓒ will not
- Ⓓ did not

Fill in the circle next to the word or words that best complete each definition.

5 Something that is odd is . . . .
- Ⓐ even
- Ⓑ far
- Ⓒ always
- Ⓓ strange

6 A word that means "at all times is" . . . .
- Ⓐ some
- Ⓑ might
- Ⓒ always
- Ⓓ far

7 A place smaller than a city is a . . . .
- Ⓐ world
- Ⓑ town
- Ⓒ state
- Ⓓ country

8 A word that means "for the reason that" is . . . .
- Ⓐ includes
- Ⓑ might
- Ⓒ because
- Ⓓ some

9 A word that means "at a distance from here" is . . . .
- Ⓐ far
- Ⓑ includes
- Ⓒ strange
- Ⓓ town

10 If a box contains something, it . . . .
- Ⓐ indents it
- Ⓑ increases it
- Ⓒ includes it
- Ⓓ invites it

WANTED: SAFETY FOR WILDLIFE

What do **walruses** in Alaska and **elephants** in Africa have in common? Both have **tusks** made of **ivory**. Hunters often kill these animals to **remove** their tusks. The ivory is sold for a lot of money. It is then carved into beautiful **objects**.

Scientists at a **laboratory** in Oregon want to stop this killing, which is against the law. They test the ivory to see if it comes from an animal that was just killed, or one that died long ago. If it is from an animal that was just killed, they destroy the ivory.

Thanks to these scientists, not as many walruses and elephants are being killed today. The hunters are learning that **crime** does not pay.

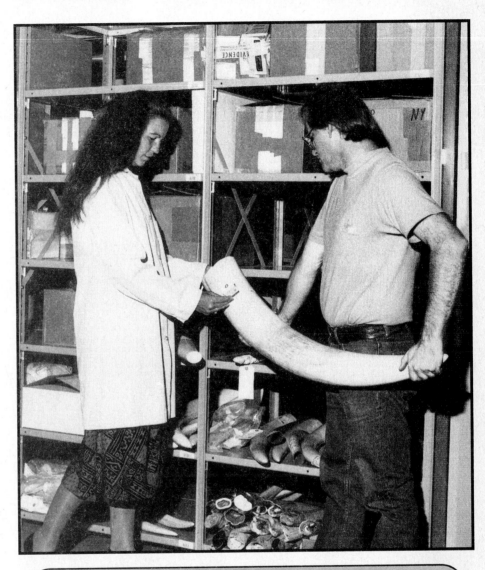

PLACING FIRST THINGS FIRST

Which event happened first?

Check the best answer.

- ◯ Scientists tested the ivory.
- ◯ Hunters killed elephants and walruses.
- ◯ Ivory was made into pretty objects.
- ◯ Hunters sold the ivory.

ABC'S PUT WORDS IN ORDER

New Words

walruses

elephants

laboratory

ivory

tusks

remove

objects

crime

Print the New Words in alphabetical order.

1. _____   5. _____

2. _____   6. _____

3. _____   7. _____

4. _____   8. _____

WORDS AND MEANINGS MATCH

Use a New Word to finish each meaning. Fill in the word shapes.

1. "To take away" means to ⬜⬜⬜⬜⬜⬜ .

2. The long teeth in elephants and walruses are ⬜⬜⬜⬜⬜ .

3. "An act that breaks the law" is a ⬜⬜⬜⬜⬜ .

4. A place where scientists work is called a ⬜⬜⬜⬜⬜⬜⬜⬜⬜⬜ .

5. Animals with tusks that live in Alaska are ⬜⬜⬜⬜⬜⬜⬜⬜ .

6. Animals with tusks that live in Africa are ⬜⬜⬜⬜⬜⬜⬜⬜⬜ .

7. The hard, white material that tusks are made of is ⬜⬜⬜⬜⬜ .

8. "Things that can be seen or touched" are ⬜⬜⬜⬜⬜⬜⬜ .

SOLVE THE MYSTERY OF THE MISSING WORDS

Print the New Word that best completes each sentence.

1. It is a _____ to hunt elephants.

2. In the past, ivory has been carved into beautiful _____ .

3. The _____ of an elephant look like long horns.

4. Some people have hunted _____ in Africa.

5. The scientists worked on the problem in their _____ .

6. This white plastic only looks like _____ .

7. The _____ of Alaska also grow tusks.

8. Please _____ your feet from that table.

SOUND WON'T HELP

Homonyms are words that sound the same but have different spellings and meanings.

pair and **pear**
blue and **blew**

Circle the correct homonyms that complete the sentences in this note.

Dear Mom and Dad,

I (eight, ate) my lunch and I (red, read) my book for an (hour, our). (Aunt, Ant) Mary called to talk to you. She will (meet, meat) you at (hour, our) house at 4:00.

Love,
Jack

ABOUT ELEPHANTS

Elephants prefer to walk single file instead of side-by-side.

Elephants are plant eaters. Wild elephants eat about 500 pounds of food a day. Elephants in zoos eat only about 150 pounds of food a day.

HEY MOM, CAN I KEEP HIM?

 You probably do not have an elephant or a walrus for a pet. Write about why these animals would not make good pets.

Use these questions to help you to think about these animals:

- Why wouldn't you want one of these animals for a pet?
    - Where do these animals live?
        - What do these animals eat?

Use three of the New Words in your writing.

LEARN MORE ABOUT HELPING ANIMALS

- *Save the Earth: An Action Handbook for Kids* by Betty Miles. (Random House, 1991)

- *Equal Rights for Animals* by Rosalind Kerven. (Franklin Watts, 1992)

- *Animal Rights — Yes or No?* by Marna A. Owen. (Lerner, 1992)

- *Kids Can Save the Animals: 101 Easy Things to Do* by Ingrid Newkirk. (Warner Books, 1991)

Save the test. Take it!

TEST-TAKING SECRETS REVEALED

Fill in the whole answer circle, but do not spend too much time on each one.

Look at each picture. Fill in the circle next to the word that best fits each picture.

1
- Ⓐ ivory
- Ⓑ elephants
- Ⓒ walruses
- Ⓓ objects

3
- Ⓐ elephants
- Ⓑ objects
- Ⓒ walruses
- Ⓓ crime

2
- Ⓐ ivory
- Ⓑ crime
- Ⓒ laboratory
- Ⓓ tusks

4
- Ⓐ tusks
- Ⓑ objects
- Ⓒ walruses
- Ⓓ crime

Read each group of words. Fill in the circle next to the word or words that mean the <u>same</u> as the underlined word.

5 <u>remove</u> the splinter
- Ⓐ take out
- Ⓑ put in
- Ⓒ paint
- Ⓓ tell about

8 <u>objects</u> on the desk
- Ⓐ books
- Ⓑ pencils
- Ⓒ things
- Ⓓ papers

6 made of <u>ivory</u>
- Ⓐ what tusks are made of
- Ⓑ wood
- Ⓒ plastic
- Ⓓ what a piano is made of

9 worked in the <u>laboratory</u>
- Ⓐ room where you sleep
- Ⓑ room where scientists work
- Ⓒ store
- Ⓓ playground

7 saw a <u>crime</u>
- Ⓐ act that breaks the law
- Ⓑ person that breaks the law
- Ⓒ movie
- Ⓓ show

10 lost its <u>tusks</u>
- Ⓐ ears
- Ⓑ noses
- Ⓒ long teeth
- Ⓓ short hair

HOUSE GETS TOO FULL
FAMILY ACTS UP

Imagine what is is like to grow up on TV in front of **millions** of people, instead of in your own **house**. The stars of "Full House" don't mind. Jodie Sweetin, who plays Stephanie, is an only **child** and loves being part of her TV **family**. Candace Cameron, who plays D.J., likes going to **school** on the "Full House" set. She works hardest on those **scenes** that let her show a more serious side.

The **twins**, Mary Kate and Ashley Olsen, take turns playing Michelle. Don't tell, but the scoop is that they're not **identical**.

Things are pretty quiet on the set until cake and ice cream appear. Then watch out!

SEARCH IS ON FOR DETAILS

Why does Candace Cameron like more serious scenes?

Check the best answer.

- ☐ She likes to feel sad.
- ☐ They make her feel happy.
- ☐ They are challenging scenes to act.
- ☐ They make her feel important.

ALPHABET HOUSE INCOMPLETE

Print the New Words in alphabetical order.

👉 Look at the beginning of each New Word. When the first two letters are the same, use the third letters.

sc<u>e</u>nt comes before **sc<u>h</u>eme**

NEW WORDS

identical

millions

school

family

scenes

house

twins

child

1. _____

2. _____

3. _____

4. _____

5. _____

6. _____

7. _____

8. _____

WORDS NEED MEANING

Use a New Word to finish each meaning. Fill in the word shapes.

1. Parts of a show are called ☐☐☐☐☐☐ .

2. Two children born at the same time to the same mother are ☐☐☐☐☐ .

3. A building where some people live is called a ☐☐☐☐☐ .

4. A person who is not an adult is called a ☐☐☐☐☐ .

5. To be exactly the same is to be ☐☐☐☐☐☐☐☐☐ .

6. The building where you learn your lessons is a ☐☐☐☐☐☐ .

7. A very large number is ☐☐☐☐☐☐☐☐ .

8. Parents, children, and other relatives make up a ☐☐☐☐☐☐ .

SENTENCE HOLES NEED FILLING

NEW WORDS

house

millions

child

family

scenes

school

twins

identical

Print the New Word that best completes each sentence.

1. I looked at _____ from the new show.

2. This pencil is _____ to mine.

3. I am the only _____ in my family.

4. There are _____ of stars in the sky.

5. Our _____ ate dinner together last night.

6. My _____ has a porch on the front.

7. Where do you go to _____ ?

8. My brother and I have fun being _____ .

FIND THE WORDS IN PUZZLE

Circle each New Word in the word search.

```
B M K F T W I N S
L I C H I L D R C
E L S C E N E S F
S L A J Q C N X A
M I D P A Y T I M
H O U S E U I B I
T N Z O W H C V L
X S D F Y S A W Y
N S C H O O L G M
```

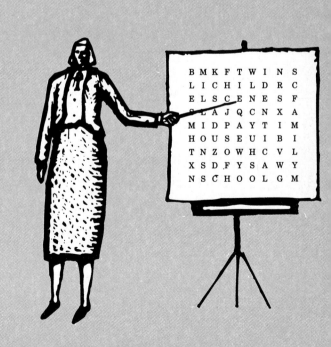

DON'T WAIT FOR RERUNS!

READ:

- *Stardust* by Alane Ferguson.
  (Bradbury Press, 1993)

- *A Kid's TV Guide: A Children's Book
  About Watching TV Intelligently*
  by Joy Wilt Berry. (Children's Press, 1982)

- *Nutty, the Movie Star* by Dean Hughes.
  (Atheneum, 1989)

- *Stage Fright, A Sebastian Barth Mystery*
  by James Howe. (Atheneum, 1986)

PLAY:

- *Lenny's Music Tunes*. (IBM CD-ROM from
  Paramount)

HOUSE FULL OF FACTS

Did you know that Scott Weinger, who plays D.J.'s boyfriend, was the voice of Aladdin in the movie *Aladdin*?

WHAT MAKES YOUR HOUSE FULL?

 Some families are big and some are small. Write about your family.

These questions will help get you started:
- How many people are in your family?

- Where does your family live?

- What does your family like to do together?

Use three of the New Words in your writing.

Finish house cleaning and take the test!

SCORE HIGHER ON TESTS

 Never leave an answer blank. Think about the question and make your very best guess.

Read each group of words. Fill in the circle next to the word or words that mean the __same__ as the underlined word.

1 new <u>house</u>
- Ⓐ parents
- Ⓑ show
- Ⓒ school
- Ⓓ home

2 <u>child</u> playing
- Ⓐ parent
- Ⓑ boy or girl
- Ⓒ teacher
- Ⓓ aunt or uncle

3 go to <u>school</u>
- Ⓐ place for learning
- Ⓑ your home
- Ⓒ full house
- Ⓓ TV show

4 <u>identical</u> faces
- Ⓐ different
- Ⓑ round
- Ⓒ long
- Ⓓ same

Read each sentence. Fill in the circle next to the word that best completes the sentence.

5 She likes to act in ____ that are funny.
- Ⓐ seams
- Ⓑ scenes
- Ⓒ scares
- Ⓓ scales

6 I cannot tell the ____ apart.
- Ⓐ twins
- Ⓑ house
- Ⓒ millions
- Ⓓ family

7 She treated me like one of her ____ .
- Ⓐ millions
- Ⓑ scenes
- Ⓒ family
- Ⓓ school

8 ____ of people watch that TV show.
- Ⓐ Twins
- Ⓑ Scenes
- Ⓒ Millions
- Ⓓ House

9 Our house is ____ to yours.
- Ⓐ identical
- Ⓑ family
- Ⓒ school
- Ⓓ millions

10 He remembers when he was a ____ .
- Ⓐ house
- Ⓑ school
- Ⓒ child
- Ⓓ family

STOP

DINE WITH DEVILS — MEALS ARE A SCREAM!

Tasmanian devils have no manners!

Those little devils! They eat off the ground and hardly chew. They **gobble** rotten meat and **swallow** the bones. They **scream** and fight over the food. They seem to **spin**, their ears turn red, and they spray a smell.

Where do you find such **creatures**? In Tasmania. That's an island **south** of Australia. These Tasmanian devils, as they are called, are as small as cats, but eat as much as lions. They have even been known to eat such things as boots and batteries.

Tasmanian devils live **alone**. When newborns are old enough, they leave their mother to start life on their own.

Those Tasmanian devils! Where are their **manners**?

BAD-MANNERED DEVILS

Where do you find Tasmanian devils?

Check the best answer.

☐ in tropical rain forests
☐ in northern California
☐ on an island south of Australia
☐ in the Sahara desert

SPIN THROUGH THE ALPHABET

Print the New Words in alphabetical order.

☞ When two words have the same first letter,
use the second letter to see which word comes first.

scar comes before **solid**
spark comes before **sweep**

1. _____   5. _____

2. _____   6. _____

3. _____   7. _____

4. _____   8. _____

New Words

manners	creatures
swallow	south
spin	gobble
scream	alone

WORDS AND MEANINGS MATCH

Use a New Word to finish each meaning. Fill in the word shapes.

1. "Polite ways of behaving" means ☐☐☐☐☐☐☐ .

2. To be by oneself is to be ☐☐☐☐☐ .

3. "To eat quickly" means to ☐☐☐☐☐☐ .

4. Another name for animals is ☐☐☐☐☐☐☐☐☐ .

5. "To turn rapidly" means to ☐☐☐☐ .

6. To take into the body through the throat is to ☐☐☐☐☐☐☐ .

7. "In the opposite direction from the North Pole" means ☐☐☐☐☐ .

8. To make a loud, shrill cry is to ☐☐☐☐☐☐ .

WORDS DISCOVERED IN GROUPS

Some words go together in **groups**. Each New Word below helps to name a group.

Circle the three words that belong in the group.

things that are <u>creatures</u>

dogs   books   cats   hamsters

things in a <u>school</u>

principal   students   teacher   banker

things in a <u>meal</u>

food   metal   meat   fruit

THE FINAL WORD ON INCOMPLETE SENTENCES

Print the New Word that best completes each sentence.

1. My aunt lives _____.

2. Tasmanian devils are strange _____.

3. I think your _____ are very good.

4. Did you ever _____ a top?

5. Why did you _____ so loudly?

6. Tasmania is _____ of Australia.

7. If you _____ your meal, you may get sick.

8. It is hard to _____ such a large pill.

TRICKY TORNADO

Tasmanian devils look like they're spinning when they scare others away, but they are really jumping quickly sideward, forward, sideward, forward as they flash their 42 sharp teeth.

OUCH!

A DEVIL OF A PET

Pretend that you have a Tasmanian devil at home for a pet. Write a report for the class to tell what your pet is like.

Use these questions to get you started:
- What do you call your pet?
- How does your pet act?
- What do you like best about your pet?

Use three of the New Words in your report.

A POUCHFUL OF DEVILS

Tasmanian devils have as many as fifty babies at one time. But the four that crawl into the mother's pouch first will be the only babies that live.

WANT TO HAVE A DEVILISHLY GOOD TIME?

READ:
- *Tasmanian Devil on Location* by Kathy Darling. (Lee and Shepard, 1992)
- *Kangaroos and Other Marsupials* by Lionel Bender. (Gloucester Press, 1988)

Don't be a devil. Take the test!

TEST-DAY TIPS TOLD

t helps to have a quiet room in which to take a test. Do your part in keeping he room quiet.

Read each sentence. Fill in the circle next to the word that best completes the sentence.

To eat quickly is to . . . .
- Ⓐ spin
- Ⓑ gobble
- Ⓒ swallow
- Ⓓ scream

2 Polite ways of acting are called . . . .
- Ⓐ grubs
- Ⓑ alone
- Ⓒ manners
- Ⓓ south

3 To be by oneself is to be . . . .
- Ⓐ alone
- Ⓑ south
- Ⓒ gobble
- Ⓓ creatures

4 To make a loud cry is to . . . .
- Ⓐ spin
- Ⓑ swallow
- Ⓒ scream
- Ⓓ spray

Read each sentence below. Fill in the circle next to the word that best completes he sentence.

5 When we dance, we ____ around in a circle.
- Ⓐ swallow
- Ⓑ scream
- Ⓒ spin
- Ⓓ spray

6 My grandparents live ____ of our town.
- Ⓐ alone
- Ⓑ south
- Ⓒ away
- Ⓓ hardly

7 My throat is sore, and it hurts to ____ .
- Ⓐ swallow
- Ⓑ walk
- Ⓒ spin
- Ⓓ gobble

8 He wants to be ____ for awhile.
- Ⓐ mature
- Ⓑ hardly
- Ⓒ south
- Ⓓ alone

9 Your parents must be pleased with your ____ .
- Ⓐ creatures
- Ⓑ manners
- Ⓒ spin
- Ⓓ scream

10 Tasmanian devils are strange ____ .
- Ⓐ creatures
- Ⓑ alone
- Ⓒ manners
- Ⓓ south

STOP

TRUE STORY ABOUT TEDDY BEARS

One day Morris Michum, a candy store owner, saw a **drawing** in the newspaper. It showed the **leader** of the United States on a hunting **trip**. The **story** said that while President Teddy Roosevelt was hunting, he saw a bear **cub**. He was about to shoot it, but couldn't harm the little bear.

Michum was happy that Roosevelt was **kind** to bears. He made a bear as a **toy** to sell at his store. He also wrote to President Roosevelt asking to name his bear Teddy. The president **replied**, "yes."

Michum's toy bears sold fast. He began to sell toys instead of candy. He became one of the largest toy makers around — The Ideal Toy Company.

WHAT'S THE CAUSE?

Why did Morris Michum stop selling candy?

Check the best answer.

◯ President Roosevelt said to stop.

◯ Nobody bought the candy.

◯ He sold toy bears instead.

◯ He ran out of candy.

New Words

drawing

leader

trip

story

cub

kind

toy

replied

Print the New Words in alphabetical order.

☞ When two words have the same first letter, use the second letter to see which word comes first.

t<u>o</u>p comes before **tr**ain

1. _____

2. _____

3. _____

4. _____

5. _____

6. _____

7. _____

8. _____

WORDS MATCH UP WITH MEANINGS

Use a New Word to finish each meaning. Fill in the word shapes.

1. "Answered" means ⬚⬚⬚⬚⬚⬚⬚ .

2. The act of traveling is called a ⬚⬚⬚⬚ .

3. To be gentle is to be ⬚⬚⬚⬚ .

4. "A picture" means a ⬚⬚⬚⬚⬚⬚⬚ .

5. A tale is a ⬚⬚⬚⬚⬚ .

6. A young bear is called a ⬚⬚⬚ .

7. The head of a group is its ⬚⬚⬚⬚⬚⬚ .

8. Something to play with is called a ⬚⬚⬚ .

HONEY

FILL IN THE MISSING WORDS

Print the New Word that best completes each sentence.

1. His favorite _____ is a truck.

2. I am taking a _____ to the beach.

3. Why haven't you _____ to the question?

4. I saw a _____ of the first teddy bear.

5. The president is the _____ of the country.

6. Thank you for being so _____ .

7. The students always enjoy hearing a _____ .

8. The small _____ looked so cute.

TEDDY BEARS HELP SOLVE PUZZLE

Use the New Words to complete the crossword puzzle.

ACROSS

3. a plaything
4. a picture
6. person who is the head of a group

DOWN

1. a happening that is told
2. helpful and friendly
3. the act of traveling
5. answered

BEAR BOOKS

- *Old Bear Tales* by Jane Hissey. (Philomel, 1988)
- *Best Friends* by Jane Hissey. (Philomel, 1989)
- *Michael Bond's Book of Bears.* (Aladdin Books, 1992)
- *My Old Teddy* by Dom Mansell. (Candlewick Press, 1992)

TOYLAND

A VISIT TO TOYLAND

Pretend that you visited a toy store that has all the kinds of toys that you like. Write a note to a friend to tell that person about the store.

Use these questions to help you get started:
- What kinds of toys does the store sell?
- What is the best toy in the store?
- What toy would you like to buy for your friend?

Use three of the New Words in your note.

THE BEAR FACTS ABOUT SOME FAMOUS BEARS

> *Winnie-the-Pooh* was written by A. A. Milne. It was named after a toy bear that belonged to his son, Christopher Robin. Christopher had named his stuffed toy "Winnie." "Pooh" was the name of a swan that Christopher liked to feed in the local park.

> *Paddington Bear* was written by Michael Bond. Paddington got his name from the Paddington Railway Station in London.

Toy with the test!

IMPROVE YOUR TEST SCORES

Get comfortable. Sit back in the chair with your feet on the floor and your test paper directly in front of you.

Read each group of words. Fill in the circle next to the word or words that mean the <u>same</u> as the underlined word.

1 followed the <u>leader</u>
- Ⓐ person who follows
- Ⓑ person who guides
- Ⓒ police officer
- Ⓓ game warden

2 read a <u>story</u>
- Ⓐ tale
- Ⓑ tail
- Ⓒ picture
- Ⓓ letter

3 saw the <u>cub</u>
- Ⓐ game
- Ⓑ box
- Ⓒ young bear
- Ⓓ adult bear

4 bought a <u>toy</u>
- Ⓐ cub
- Ⓑ trip
- Ⓒ story
- Ⓓ plaything

5 <u>kind</u> to animals
- Ⓐ angry
- Ⓑ friendly
- Ⓒ cruel
- Ⓓ brave

6 a vacation <u>trip</u>
- Ⓐ camp
- Ⓑ tent
- Ⓒ travels
- Ⓓ beach

Read each sentence below. Fill in the circle next to the word that means the <u>same</u> as the underlined word.

7 To be <u>kind</u> is to be—
- Ⓐ selfish
- Ⓑ hard
- Ⓒ gentle
- Ⓓ loud

8 A <u>drawing</u> is a—
- Ⓐ game
- Ⓑ letter
- Ⓒ book
- Ⓓ picture

9 If people <u>replied</u>, they—
- Ⓐ made
- Ⓑ answered
- Ⓒ moved
- Ⓓ bought

10 To take a <u>trip</u> is to make a—
- Ⓐ journey
- Ⓑ fall
- Ⓒ circle
- Ⓓ picture

SCREAMING GUESTS
THROW HANDS UP IN AIR

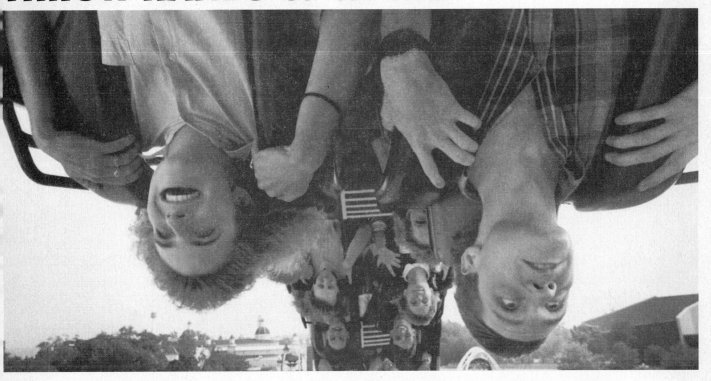

"I thought the bottom fell out!" screams rider.

There's a slow **climb** to the top and a **zooming** drop to the bottom. "Scream machines" **thrill** visitors in Cedar Point, a **park** in Sandusky, Ohio. The first Cedar Point coaster, built in 1892, was 25 feet tall and ran ten miles per hour. "Raptor," its eleventh and newest coaster, is 137 feet tall. It will carry you at 57 miles per hour – *upside down*!

The first roller coaster was a **slippery** wooden slide covered with ice. It was built in Russia in the 1400s. The first in the United States was built at Coney Island in 1884. Today you can ride both **metal** and **wooden** coasters.

Some coasters, like Cedar Point's "Magnum XL-200," can go 70 miles per hour. Would you like to go on one of these **speedy** rides?

ORDER THE ROLLER COASTERS

Which of these was made first?

Check the best answer.

❏ the first Cedar Point roller coaster

❏ the wooden slide in Russia

❏ the Coney Island roller coaster

❏ Cedar Point's "Magnum XL-200"

ALPHABET TAKES WORDS ON A RIDE

Print the New Words in alphabetical order.

☞ Look at the first letters of each New Word. When the first letters are the same, use the second letters.

slime comes before **sp**ace

New Words

climb

zooming

thrill

park

slippery

metal

wooden

speedy

1. _____

2. _____

3. _____

4. _____

5. _____

6. _____

7. _____

8. _____

COAST THROUGH THESE MEANINGS

Use a New Word to finish each meaning. Fill in the word shapes.

1. To be fast is to be ⬚⬚⬚⬚⬚⬚ .

2. A word meaning "made of wood" is ⬚⬚⬚⬚⬚⬚ .

3. Flying very fast through the air is ⬚⬚⬚⬚⬚⬚⬚ .

4. A place where you can rest and have fun is a ⬚⬚⬚⬚ .

5. "To make excited" means to ⬚⬚⬚⬚⬚⬚ .

6. Going up to a high point is a ⬚⬚⬚⬚⬚ .

7. A hard material used to make cars is ⬚⬚⬚⬚⬚ .

8. A place where you can slide is ⬚⬚⬚⬚⬚⬚⬚⬚ .

84

COAST TO A COMPLETE SENTENCE

Print the New Word that best completes each sentence.

1. My favorite _____ is Cedar Point.

2. Dad stirred the fudge with a shiny _____ spoon.

3. Rides on roller coasters always _____ us.

4. You were so _____ I could not keep up with you.

5. The sidewalk was _____ after the rain.

6. I saw a falling star _____ across the sky.

7. The _____ table was very heavy.

8. That was some _____ up that hill!

COASTER CAUSES SCRAMBLE

Unscramble the New Words and print them on the lines.

1. downeo _____

2. krpa _____

3. tmlae _____

4. eypsed _____

5. hltrli _____

6. yplsipre _____

7. blmic _____

8. ozmgino _____

NEW WORDS

climb   slippery

zooming   metal

thrill   wooden

park   speedy

FUN IN THE SUN

Plan a day at your favorite park. Write several sentences telling the things you would like to do on this day. Share your sentences with a friend. Would your friend like to spend the day with you?

These questions might give you some ideas:
- What ride do you like the most?
- Whom do you want to take with you to the park?
- What will be the first thing you do in the park?

Use three of the New Words in your sentences.

The "Raptor" flips passengers and spirals them upside-down into a 180-degree roll.

EXPLORE YOUR
UPS AND DOWNS

READ:
- *The Macmillan Book of How Things Work* by Michael and Marcia Folsom. (Macmillan, 1987)
- *Which Way Is Up?* by Gail Kay Haines. (Atheneum, 1987)

WATCH:
- *A Dream Called Walt Disney World.* (Walt Disney Home Video)

PLAY:
- *DinoParkTycoon.* (IBM software from MECC)
- *Even More Incredible Machines.* (IBM software from Sierra-On-Line)

WILD FACTS
To build "The Rattler," the world's tallest roller coaster, it took 857,000 feet of wood, 159,000 bolts, 23,500 pounds of nails, and 1,925 cubic yards of concrete.

You must be this tall to take the test!

SECRETS TO SUCCESS ON TESTS

Go back to the story to see how the key word is used there. This will help you to see its meaning.

Read each sentence. Fill in the circle next to the word that best completes the sentence.

1 I fell on the ____ sidewalk.
- Ⓐ zooming
- Ⓑ metal
- Ⓒ slippery
- Ⓓ wooden

2 A key is made of ____ .
- Ⓐ wooden
- Ⓑ metal
- Ⓒ flour
- Ⓓ sticks

3 It is a long ____ to the top of that hill.
- Ⓐ thrill
- Ⓑ walk
- Ⓒ hear
- Ⓓ climb

4 The ____ rides at the park are his favorites.
- Ⓐ speedy
- Ⓑ sticks
- Ⓒ climb
- Ⓓ walk

Fill in the circle next to the word that best completes each definition.

5 To make excited is to . . . .
- Ⓐ tell
- Ⓑ throw
- Ⓒ thrill
- Ⓓ trill

6 Something that is moving very fast is . . . .
- Ⓐ metal
- Ⓑ zooming
- Ⓒ wooden
- Ⓓ slippery

7 An area set aside for enjoyment is a . . . .
- Ⓐ coaster
- Ⓑ machine
- Ⓒ climb
- Ⓓ park

8 To be made of wood is to be . . . .
- Ⓐ would
- Ⓑ wooden
- Ⓒ wonder
- Ⓓ woolly

9 Something that is fast is . . . .
- Ⓐ slippery
- Ⓑ wooden
- Ⓒ metal
- Ⓓ speedy

10 The act of going up is a . . . .
- Ⓐ thrill
- Ⓑ park
- Ⓒ climb
- Ⓓ coaster

STOP

MEDICINE CABINET FOUND IN BACKYARD

WARNING • CAUTION • WARNING • CAUTION
Never eat a plant without an adult present. Some plants are poisonous.

What do you do when you have a cold? What about a cut finger? You may go to the **drugstore** for vitamin pills or bandages. Or, you may look in your **backyard**.

Some of nature's best **vitamin** pills are dandelion greens and rose hips. Rose hips have a lot of vitamin C. They will be very popular if there is ever a **shortage** of **citrus** fruits. And, if you get a cut or a burn, the aloe plant will help to heal your **wound**.

Today many gardens and **meadows** hold a **harvest** of cures for common problems. Take a second look. Your garden could be worth a *mint*.

WHAT'S THE CAUSE

Why might people eat rose hips?

Check the best answer.

- ❑ They want to get vitamin C.
- ❑ They are too thin in their hips.
- ❑ They like oranges.
- ❑ They want to heal their wounds.

ABC'S PUT WORDS IN ORDER

Print the New Words in alphabetical order.

NEW WORDS

drugstore
backyard
vitamin
shortage
citrus
wound
meadows
harvest

1. _____

2. _____

3. _____

4. _____

5. _____

6. _____

7. _____

8. _____

WORDS SEARCH FOR MEANINGS

Use a New Word to finish each meaning. Fill in the word shapes.

1. The crop that is picked is called the ⬜⬜⬜⬜⬜⬜⬜ .

2. The grass and dirt behind a house is the ⬜⬜⬜⬜⬜⬜⬜⬜ .

3. Something needed by our bodies is a ⬜⬜⬜⬜⬜⬜ .

4. Oranges are a fruit called ⬜⬜⬜⬜⬜⬜ .

5. A place where medicine is sold is a ⬜⬜⬜⬜⬜⬜⬜⬜⬜ .

6. A cut or other injury is a ⬜⬜⬜⬜⬜ .

7. Fields of flowers or grass are called ⬜⬜⬜⬜⬜⬜⬜ .

8. "A lack of something" means a ⬜⬜⬜⬜⬜⬜⬜⬜ .

WORDS FILL SENTENCE HOLES

Print the New Word that best completes each sentence.

NEW WORDS

drugstore
backyard
vitamin
shortage
citrus
wound
meadows
harvest

1. My mother takes a _____ pill every morning.

2. Come and play in my _____ .

3. We gathered the _____ at the end of the summer

4. My dad received a _____ in the war.

5. The grass in the _____ was growing very high.

6. Lemons are a _____ fruit.

7. The store had a _____ of milk today.

8. Will you go to the _____ for me?

PICK FROM SYNONYM GARDEN

Synonyms are words with nearly the same meaning.
big and **large**   **begin** and **start**

Pick the words from the "Synonym Garden." Draw a line between each word and its synony

 lid   story   peek   big   spin

large   top   look   twirl   tale

PLANTING FACTS

➤ Native Americans made it through many hard winters eating the bark of white pine trees.

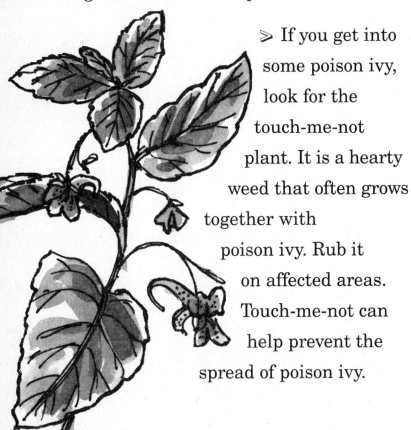

➤ If you get into some poison ivy, look for the touch-me-not plant. It is a hearty weed that often grows together with poison ivy. Rub it on affected areas. Touch-me-not can help prevent the spread of poison ivy.

TIRED OF SWATTING MOSQUITOES?

Crushed pennyroyal, a strongly scented plant, on your skin will solve the problem.

NEW CURE-ALL FOUND

Imagine that you are a scientist and you have created a new medicine. Write a story about what this medicine is and how you discovered it.

Use these questions to help you get started:
• What illness does your medicine cure?
• How do you make your medicine?
• Where do you find the ingredients for your medicine?

Use three of the New Words in your writing.

Recover for the test!

TAKE YOUR PICK READ:

• *Mud Grape Pie* by Catherine S. Cardinal. (Golden Gate, 1991)
• *Plants That Harm and Heal* by Anne O. Dowden. (Harper Collins, 1994)
• *A Child's Book of Wildflowers* by M.A. Kelly. (Four Winds Press, 1992)
• *Eyewitness Books: Plants* by David Burnie (Knopf, 1989)

TEST YOUR BEST

Look over your test a last time to make sure you did not miss any questions and that your answers can be easily read by the teacher.

Read each group of words. Fill in the circle next to the word or words that mean the <u>same</u> as the underlined word.

1   in my <u>backyard</u>
- Ⓐ   park
- Ⓑ   playground
- Ⓒ   area behind a house
- Ⓓ   area in front of a house

2   ate <u>citrus</u> fruit
- Ⓐ   tomatoes and corn
- Ⓑ   oranges and lemons
- Ⓒ   bananas and pears
- Ⓓ   corn and peas

3   heal the <u>wound</u>
- Ⓐ   feelings
- Ⓑ   bumps
- Ⓒ   cut
- Ⓓ   headache

4   the corn <u>harvest</u>
- Ⓐ   on the cob
- Ⓑ   gathered crop
- Ⓒ   dish
- Ⓓ   meal

5   go to the <u>drugstore</u>
- Ⓐ   medicine store
- Ⓑ   toy store
- Ⓒ   food store
- Ⓓ   tire store

6   because of a <u>shortage</u>
- Ⓐ   short
- Ⓑ   lack
- Ⓒ   long
- Ⓓ   shock

Read each sentence. Fill in the circle next to the word or words that best complete the sentence.

7   Do you take ____ pills?
- Ⓐ   harvest   Ⓒ   drugstore
- Ⓑ   vitamin   Ⓓ   citrus

8   We walked through ____ the whole day long.
- Ⓐ   meadows   Ⓒ   harvest
- Ⓑ   vitamins   Ⓓ   wounds

9   There is a ____ of paper so do not waste it.
- Ⓐ   harvest   Ⓒ   meadows
- Ⓑ   drugstore   Ⓓ   shortage

10   He received that ____ in an accident.
- Ⓐ   vitamin   Ⓒ   wound
- Ⓑ   shortage   Ⓓ   citrus

(STOP)

STAMPS COME FROM FAR-AWAY LANDS

"I'm stuck on stamps!"

Stamp collecting is a **hobby** that is fun and interesting. There are **stamps** about almost anything. You may **collect** stamps from around the world. Or you may collect stamps about special **subjects** such as dinosaurs, space, the Olympics, and musicians.

How can you start stamp collecting? It's easy. Just **save** the stamps on your family's mail, and ask your family members to save the stamps from **mail** they get at work. You may also want to buy interesting stamps at the post office.

When you have a lot of stamps, **sort** them and put them into a notebook. As your collection grows, you'll spend many **wonderful** hours at your new hobby.

WHAT'S THE REASON?

Why do people save stamps?

Check the best answer.

- ◯ to mail letters
- ◯ to visit different places
- ◯ to enjoy as a hobby
- ◯ to fill notebooks

ABC'S PUT WORDS IN ORDER

Print the New Words in alphabetical order.

New Words
wonderful
hobby
stamps
collect
subjects
save
mail
sort

☞ When two words have the same first letter, use the second letter to see which word comes first.

s<u>a</u>le comes before s<u>u</u>ch

1. _____   5. _____

2. _____   6. _____

3. _____   7. _____

4. _____   8. _____

WORDS AND MEANINGS MATCH UP

Use a New Word to finish each meaning. Fill in the word shapes.

1. "To bring together in one place" means to ⬚⬚⬚⬚⬚⬚⬚ .

2. Letters and packages brought to your home are called ⬚⬚⬚⬚ .

3. A way to spend your free time is called a ⬚⬚⬚⬚⬚ .

4. Small pieces of paper that are stuck on mail to pay for sending it are called ⬚⬚⬚⬚⬚⬚ .

5. Things to study and read about are called ⬚⬚⬚⬚⬚⬚⬚⬚ .

6. "To keep for some other time" means to ⬚⬚⬚⬚ .

7. Something that is excellent is ⬚⬚⬚⬚⬚⬚⬚⬚⬚ .

8. "To separate by kinds" means to ⬚⬚⬚⬚ .

PUT YOUR STAMP ON THESE SENTENCES

Print the New Word that best completes each sentence.

. I will _____ my stamps according to year.

. That is a _____ book that I have read many times.

. We _____ stamps from all around the world.

. Carlos told us all about his new _____ .

. I want to _____ that article about animals.

. The _____ comes after lunch.

. I put the _____ on the letters.

. What _____ do you like to read about?

THE SEARCH IS ON • • • • • • • • • •

Circle each New Word in the word search.

New Words
wonderful
hobby
stamps
collect
subjects
save
mail
sort

O	B	W	J	Y	K	M	Z	L
N	H	O	B	B	Y	E	S	P
X	I	N	H	M	J	G	T	A
I	M	D	S	A	V	E	A	F
C	H	E	W	I	U	B	M	E
S	O	R	T	L	A	G	P	Q
L	S	F	R	V	F	C	S	D
D	S	U	B	J	E	C	T	S
C	O	L	L	E	C	T	E	T

WRITE AND READ MORE ABOUT STAMPS

For a free catalog of products for stamp collecting, write to Philatelic Sales Division, U.S. Postal Service, P.O. Box 449997, Kansas City, MO 64144-9997.

BOOKS:
- *Collecting Stamps* by Stephen Holder. (Silver Burdett, 1979,)
- *Stamps* by Michael Briggs. (Random House, 1993)
- *Stamps! A Young Collector's Guide* by Brenda Ralph Lewis. (Lodestar Books, 1991)

A HOBBY OF MY OWN

Do you have a hobby? Or is there one you would like to start? Write about a hobby that you would like to have.

Use these questions to help you get started:
- What would your hobby be?
- Why would you like to have this hobby?
- How could you share this hobby with a friend?

Use three of the New Words in your writing.

THE ELVIS VOTE

In 1993, the post office let people vote on whether a stamp should picture musician Elvis Presley when he was young or when he was older. People voted for the stamp to show the picture of the young Elvis.

Put your stamp on the tes

TEST-TAKING SECRETS REVEALED

When looking for a word that means the same as another, replace the given word with your choice to see if it makes sense.

Read each group of words. Fill in the circle next to the word or words that mean the <u>*same*</u> *as the underlined word*

1 <u>save</u> this paper
- Ⓐ draw on
- Ⓑ write on
- Ⓒ keep
- Ⓓ take

2 bought <u>stamps</u>
- Ⓐ postage
- Ⓑ paper
- Ⓒ books
- Ⓓ pictures

3 get the <u>mail</u>
- Ⓐ paper and pencils
- Ⓑ letters and packages
- Ⓒ books
- Ⓓ games

4 all kinds of <u>subjects</u>
- Ⓐ things that are talked about
- Ⓑ things you buy
- Ⓒ books
- Ⓓ letters

5 <u>sort</u> the letters
- Ⓐ arrange by kind
- Ⓑ put together
- Ⓒ trace
- Ⓓ draw

6 a <u>wonderful</u> time
- Ⓐ long
- Ⓑ sad
- Ⓒ marvelous
- Ⓓ short

Read each sentence below. Fill in the circle next to the word or words that best complete each definition.

7 To <u>sort</u> is to—
- Ⓐ draw
- Ⓑ separate
- Ⓒ write
- Ⓓ make

8 To <u>collect</u> is to—
- Ⓐ make
- Ⓑ gather
- Ⓒ sell
- Ⓓ put

9 <u>Hobby</u> is—
- Ⓐ jobs
- Ⓑ work
- Ⓒ spare-time activity
- Ⓓ summer-time work

10 To be <u>wonderful</u> is to be—
- Ⓐ big
- Ⓑ small
- Ⓒ awesome
- Ⓓ finished

DON'T BE FOOLED BY THESE TRICKY CREATURES

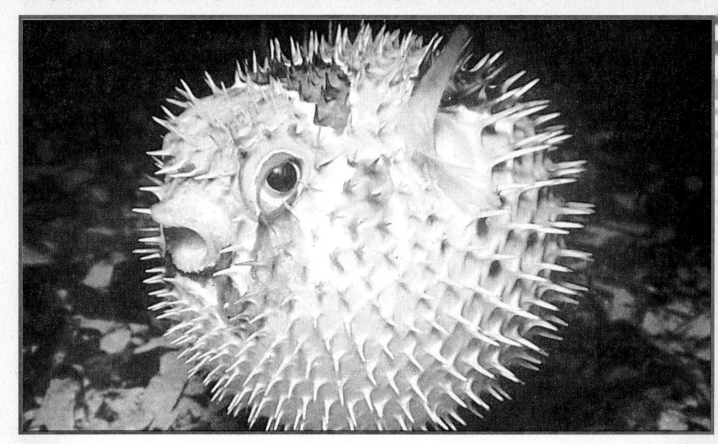

Do creatures like **fish** and caterpillars celebrate Halloween? The porcupine fish uses **tricks** to **scare** other fish away. This fish looks **harmless** most of the time. Then it drinks a lot of water to look like a balloon with sharp points. Other fish decide to eat something else.

One kind of caterpillar can make itself look like a **snake**. It has marks on its **bottom**. When an animal gets too close, it turns itself over and pretends to be a scary snake. The trick works. This caterpillar does not become a tasty **meal**.

Next time you put on a **mask** or a costume, think of those creatures that have to dress up every day.

GETTING TO THE POINT

Why do other fish not eat the porcupine fish?

Check the best answer.

◯ Its marks scare them away.

◯ It looks like a balloon with sharp points.

◯ It looks like a snake.

◯ It looks harmless.

KEEPING WORDS IN ORDER

Print the New Words in alphabetical order.

☞ When two words have the same first letter, use the second letter to see which word comes first.

sc**arf** comes before **sn**ail   **m**ake comes before **me**lt

New Words
tricks
scare
snake
bottom
mask
fish
harmless
meal

1. _____

2. _____

3. _____

4. _____

5. _____

6. _____

7. _____

8. _____

NO TRICKS TO WORDS AND MEANINGS

Use a New Word to finish each meaning. Fill in the word shapes.

1. Something that hides or disguises is a ☐☐☐☐ .

2. If something will not hurt you, it is ☐☐☐☐☐☐☐☐ .

3. The food that you eat at one time is called a ☐☐☐☐ .

4. A long thin animal that lives mostly on land is a ☐☐☐☐☐ .

5. The part of something that is underneath is called its ☐☐☐☐☐☐ .

6. An animal that lives in water is a ☐☐☐☐ .

7. To frighten is to ☐☐☐☐☐ .

8. Some things that are done to fool people are called ☐☐☐☐☐☐ .

99

MISSING WORDS  MASK MEANINGS

Print the New Word that best completes each sentence.

NEW WORDS

tricks

scare

snake

bottom

mask

fish

harmless

meal

1. I can see the _____ in the clear water.

2. Some people were afraid of the _____ .

3. Do you play _____ on your friends on April Fool's Day?

4. The little bear cub looks _____ .

5. Don't _____ away the birds.

6. I ate my _____ and then went to bed.

7. He wore a beard as a _____ to the costume part

8. My socks were at the _____ of the drawer.

UNSCRAMBLED LETTERS FORM NEW WORDS

Unscramble the New Words and print them on the lines.

1. laem _____

2. ksean _____

3. craes _____

4. ksma _____

5. stkcir _____

6. tobmot _____

7. smherlsa _____

8. shif _____

TRICK OR TREAT

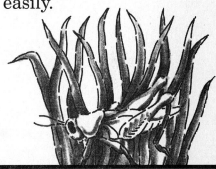 Do you have a favorite costume that you or someone you know wore for a special occasion? Write about the costume.

Use these questions to help you remember:
• What did the costume look like?
• Why did you or that person choose it?
• What did people say when they saw it?

Use three of the New Words in your writing.

SCORE HIGHER ON TESTS

Decide the meaning of any underlined words before you look at the answer choices.

Look at each picture. Fill in the circle next to the word that best fits each picture.

1
Ⓐ tricks
Ⓑ scare
Ⓒ mask
Ⓓ snake

3
Ⓐ mask
Ⓑ snake
Ⓒ tricks
Ⓓ scare

2
Ⓐ snake
Ⓑ fish
Ⓒ tricks
Ⓓ mask

4
Ⓐ fish
Ⓑ bottom
Ⓒ tricks
Ⓓ meal

Read each sentence. Fill in the circle next to the word that best completes the sentence.

5 Do not play ____ on your sister.
Ⓐ mask
Ⓑ tricks
Ⓒ snake
Ⓓ scare

7 Why do you want to ____ him?
Ⓐ snake
Ⓑ scare
Ⓒ wear
Ⓓ decide

9 I found a ____ in my garden.
Ⓐ fish
Ⓑ harmless
Ⓒ meal
Ⓓ snake

6 My dog is ____.
Ⓐ bottom
Ⓑ tricks
Ⓒ fish
Ⓓ harmless

8 There is sand on the ____ of the lake.
Ⓐ bottom
Ⓑ fish
Ⓒ water
Ⓓ animals

10 Breakfast is the first ____ of my day.
Ⓐ fish
Ⓑ meal
Ⓒ tricks
Ⓓ scare

Pronunciation Key

Letters	Show the Sound of	Written as
a	cat	KAT
ah	odd	AHD
ahr	bar	BAHR
aw	lawn	LAWN
ay	pay	PAY
b	bib	BIB
ch	chip	CHIP
d	deed	DEED
e	pet	PET
ee	bee	BEE
er	care	KER
eye	island	EYE luhnd
f	fast	FAST
g	gag	GAG
h	hat	HAT
i	pit	PIT
ir	dear	DIR
j	joke	JOHK
k	kit	KIT
l	lid	LID
m	man	MAN
n	no	NOH
ng	thing	THING
oh	go	GOH
oo	moon	MOON
or	store	STOR
ow	out	OWT
oy	joy	JOY
p	pop	PAHP
r	rat	RAT
s	see	SEE
sh	ship	SHIP
t	tin	TIN
th	thing	THING
th	then	THEN
u	book	BUK
uh	cut	KUHT
ur	her	HUR
v	vase	VAYS
w	with	WITH
y	yet	YET
z	zebra	ZEE bruh
zh	vision	VIZH uhn

GLOSSARY

A a

ac•com•plish (ah KAHM plish) *v.* to succeed in doing something

a•dored (ah DORD) *v.* thought very highly of

a•lone (ah LOHN) *adv.* by oneself

al•ways (AWL wayz) *adv.* all the time

an•i•mals (AN i mahlz) *n.* living creatures

art•ist (AHRT ist) *n.* a person who paints, draws, or carves figures

art•ists (AHRT ists) *n.* people who paint pictures

as•tro•naut (AS truh nawt) *n.* a person who travels in space

B b

back•yard (BAK yahrd) *n.* the grass and dirt behind a house

be•cause (bee KAWZ) *conj.* for the reason that

be•comes (bee KUHMZ) *v.* comes to be

be•hind (bee HEYEND) *prep.* in back of

bot•tom (BAHT uhm) *n.* the part of something that is underneath

breathe (BREETH) *v.* to take air in and out of your body

but•ter•fly (BUHT ur fleye) *n.* a pretty insect with wings

C c

care (KER) *v.* to pay attention to another's needs

carved (KAHRVD) *v.* cut or chipped to form something

cat•er•pil•lar (KAT ur pil ur) **n.** a worm that later becomes a butterfly

caves (KAYVZ) **n.** openings in the side of a hill or beneath the ground

chang•es (CHAYNJ iz) **v.** turns into something else; replaces

child (CHEYELD) **n.** a person who is not an adult

cit•rus (SI truhs) **adj.** fruit such as oranges or lemons

clean (KLEEN) **adj.** not dirty

climb (KLEYEM) **n.** going up to a high point

co•coon (kuh KOON) **n.** the place where a caterpillar turns into a butterfly

col•lect (kuh LEKT) **v.** to bring together in one place

col•lege (KAHL ij) **n.** a school for students after high school

com•ic (KAHM ik) **n.** a performer who tells jokes

cool (KOOL) **adj.** not warm but not very cold

cracks (KRAKS) **n.** breaks or openings in a surface

crea•tures (KREE churz) **n.** another name for animals

crime (KREYEM) **n.** an act that breaks the law

crops (KRAHPS) **n.** plants that grow on a farm

cub (KUHB) **n.** a young bear

cu•ri•ous (KYUR ee uhs) **adj.** wanting very much to learn

D d

dark (DAHRK) **adj.** not light

doc•tor (DAHK tur) **n.** a person who takes care of people when they are sick

draw•ing (DRAW ing) **n.** a picture

drib•ble (DRIB uhl) **v.** to bounce a ball

drug•store (DRUHG stor) **n.** a place where medicine is sold

dust (DUHST) **n.** fine powder

E e

eels (EELZ) **n.** fish that look like snakes

el•e•phants (EL uh fuhnts) **n.** animals with tusks that live in Africa

en•dan•gered (en DAYN jurd) **adj.** something that is in danger

F f

fam•i•ly (FAM uh lee) **n.** parents, children, and other relatives

far (FAHR) **adv.** not near

fins (FINZ) **n.** part of a fish that is used for swimming

fish (FISH) **n.** an animal that lives in water

fix (FIKS) **v.** to repair

fresh (FRESH) **adj.** water that is not salty

G g

gi•ant (JEYE uhnt) **adj.** very large

gob•ble (GAHB uhl) **v.** to eat quickly

grown (GROHN) **adj.** finished getting big

H h

hangs (HANGZ) **v.** sags down; droops

harm•less (HAHRM les) **adj.** not able to hurt you

har•vest (HAHR vest) **n.** the crop that is picked

heard (HURD) **v.** listened to

hob•by (HAHB ee) **n.** a way to spend your free time

hon•or (AHN ur) **v.** to give special respect to

house (HOWS) **n.** a building where some people live

I i

i•de•a (eye DEE uh) **n.** something you think of

i•den•ti•cal (eye DEN ti kuhl) **adj.** to be exactly the same

il•lus•tra•ted (IL uh strayt ed) **v.** drew pictures to go with

in•cludes (in KLOODZ) **v.** contains in a group

in•stead (in STED) **prep.** in place of

in•vent•ed (in VENT ed) **v.** made something new

is•land (EYE luhnd) **n.** land circled by water

i•vo•ry (EYE vuh ree) **n.** the hard, white material that tusks are made of

K k

kind (KEYEND) **adj.** to be gentle

L l

lab•o•ra•to•ry (LAB ruh tor ee) **n.** a place where scientists work

lead•er (LEED ur) **n.** the head of a group

leis (LAYZ) **n.** wreaths of flowers worn around the neck

light (LEYET) **n.** what all stars give off

long (LAWNG) **adj.** something that extends over a distance

look•ing (LUK ing) **v.** searching

M m

mail (MAYL) **n.** letters and packages brought to your home

ma•jor (MAY jur) **adj.** very important

man•ners (MAN urz) **n.** polite ways of behaving

map (MAP) **n.** a drawing of all or part of the Earth's surface

mask (MASK) **n.** something that hides or disguises

math•e•mat•ics (math uh MAT iks) **n.** the study of numbers

mead•ows (MED ohz) **n.** fields of flowers or grass

meal (MEEL) **n.** the food that you eat at one time

meas•ure (MEZH uhr) **v.** to find the size of something

med•i•cine (MED uh sin) **n.** something that makes you better when you are sick

mem•ber (MEM bur) **n.** one of a team of people

met•al (MET uhl) **adj.** a hard material used to make cars

mi•cro•scope (MEYE kroh skohp) **n.** something that makes tiny things seem bigger when you look through it

might (MEYET) **v.** may possibly

mil•lions (MIL yuhnz) **n.** a very large number

mu•sic (MYOO zik) **n.** songs and tunes

N n

night (NEYET) **n.** not day

O o

ob•jects (AHB jekts) **n.** things that can be seen or touched

o•pen•ing (OH puh ning) **n.** the beginning of a story

P p

park (PAHRK) **n.** a place where you can rest and have fun

per•fect (PUR fekt) **adj.** someone or something that has no faults

pet (PET) **n.** an animal that is kept at home

pool (POOL) **n.** a puddle of water

prob•lems (PRAHB lemz) **n.** things that are troublesome or are hard to understand

pub•lish (PUHB lish) **v.** to make a book

R r

read•ing (REED ing) **v.** understanding written words

re•move (ree MOOV) **v.** to take away

re•plied (ree PLEYED) **v.** answered

right (REYET) **adj.** correct or with no mistakes

rock (RAHK) **n.** a large piece of stone

S s

safe (SAYF) **adj.** free from danger

save (SAYV) **v.** to keep for some other time

scare (SKER) **v.** to frighten

scenes (SEENZ) **n.** parts of a show

school (SKOOL) **n.** a building where you learn your lessons

sci•ence (SEYE ens) **n.** the study of Earth and everything around us

scream (SKREEM) **v.** to make a loud, shrill cry

script (SKRIPT) **n.** a written form of a play or movie

sculp•ture (SKUHLP chur) **n.** something carved or molded

se•cret (SEE kret) **n.** something you do not tell others

se•lec•ted (se LEKT ed) **v.** to be chosen from among many

short (SHORT) **adj.** not tall

short•age (SHORT ij) **n.** a lack of something

shut•tle (SHUHT uhl) **n.** a vehicle that goes from Earth to space and back

sight (SEYET) **n.** something you see

sky (SKEYE) **n.** place where the sun shines

slip•per•y (SLIP uh ree) **adj.** able to cause sliding

snake (SNAYK) **n.** a long thin animal that lives mostly on land

some (SUHM) **adj.** a certain number of

sort (SORT) **v.** to separate by kinds

south (SOWTH) **n.** in the opposite direction from the North Pole

speed•y (SPEED ee) **adj.** fast

spin (SPIN) **v.** to turn rapidly

stamps (STAMPS) **n.** small pieces of paper that are stuck on mail to pay for sending it

star (STAHR) **n.** an important actor

stone (STOHN) **n.** a small piece of hard mineral

sto•ry (STOR ee) **n.** a tale

strange (STRAYNJ) **adj.** unusual

streets (STREETS) **n.** pavement where cars drive

stu•dents (STOOD nts) **n.** people who go to school

sub•jects (SUHB jekts) **n.** things to study and read about

swal•low (SWAH loh) **v.** to take into the body through the throat

T t

thin (THIN) *adj.* not thick

thrill (THRIL) *v.* to make excited

town (TOWN) *n.* a small city

toy (TOY) *n.* something to play with

traf•fic (TRAF ik) *n.* cars and trucks on a road

tricks (TRIKS) *n.* things that are done to fool people

trip (TRIP) *n.* the act of traveling

tusks (TUHSKS) *n.* the long teeth in elephants and walruses

twice (TWEYES) *adv.* two times

twins (TWINZ) *n.* two children born at the same time to the same mother

V v

val•ley (VAL ee) *n.* land between two hills

vis•i•tors (VIZ it urz) *n.* people who come to visit

vi•ta•min (VEYET ah min) *adj.* something needed by our bodies

W w

wal•rus•es (WAWL ruhs ez) *n.* animals with tusks that live in Alaska

won•der•ful (WUHN dur fuhl) *adj.* excellent

wood•en (WUD uhn) *adj.* made of wood

work (WURK) *n.* something to be done, especially as part of one's job

worm (WURM) *n.* a long, thin, crawling animal

wound (WOOND) *n.* a cut or other injury

writ•ers (REYET urz) *n.* people who put their ideas on paper

writ•ten (RIT uhn) *v.* put in writing

wrote (ROHT) *v.* told in writing

Z z

zoom•ing (ZOOM ing) *adj.* flying very fast through the air

Answer Key

The Shocking Truth About Eels
pages 3-7

Readers Look for Details
in South America

ABC Order Found
1. animals
2. eels
3. fins
4. fresh
5. long
6. measure
7. short
8. thin

Word Match Puts Meanings in Their Place
1. eels
2. fins
3. thin
4. fresh
5. short
6. long
7. animals
8. measure

Completed Sentences Give Shocking Results
1. eels
2. fins
3. short
4. long
5. thin
6. fresh
7. animals
8. measure

New Words Form Super Groups
1. bear, dog, sheep
2. inches, feet, meters
3. fish, rockets, divers

Secrets to Success on Tests
1. B
2. C
3. D
4. A
5. D
6. B
7. B
8. C
9. B
10. B

Run, Dribble, Jump, Shoot
pages 8-12

Details Slam-dunked
being selected to play with the Harlem Globetrotters

Order in the Court
1. accomplish
2. college
3. dribble
4. major
5. member
6. perfect
7. selected
8. twice

Getting in Shape
1. college
2. member
3. selected
4. major
5. perfect
6. accomplish
7. dribble
8. twice

Completing the Sentences
1. college
2. perfect
3. dribble
4. accomplish
5. major
6. twice
7. selected
8. member

Searching for a Winner
```
H P E R F E C T A T L T S H M
W N S B I S O W Z B U M G D L
A C C O M P L I S H L E N F M
G V F R A Q L C Y K E M C K F
C N J M J O E E D R I B B L E
U E A K O L G N X O V E Z R B
O J C X R P E W P G D R A H F
I D S E L E C T E D J E Y Q I
```

Score Higher on Tests
1. C
2. B
3. A
4. C
5. D
6. B
7. D
8. B
9. A
10. C

Ten, Nine, Eight . . . Blastoff!
pages 13-17

That's the Idea
She teaches math and science.

Alphabet Keeps Words in Order
1. astronaut
2. doctor
3. mathematics
4. medicine
5. microscope
6. science
7. shuttle
8. students

Words Match Meanings
1. mathematics
2. medicine
3. shuttle
4. science
5. doctor
6. microscope
7. astronaut
8. students

Words Complete Sentences
1. astronaut
2. medicine
3. microscope
4. science
5. shuttle
6. students
7. doctor
8. mathematics

Sound Isn't Everything
1. d
2. c
3. b
4. a
5. b
6. d
7. a
8. c

Test-day Tips Told
1. B
2. D
3. A
4. B
5. C
6. B
7. A
8. D
9. B
10. D

Snails Sing Hawaiians to Sleep at Night
pages 18-22

Detail the Snails
in Hawaii

The ABC's of Snails
1. crops
2. endangered
3. honor
4. instead
5. island
6. leis
7. opening
8. valley

Shaping Up the Meanings
1. crops
2. honor
3. island
4. opening
5. leis
6. valley
7. instead
8. endangered

Missing Words Complete Sentences
1. leis
2. opening
3. honor
4. island
5. endangered
6. valley
7. instead
8. crops

Story Words Unscrambled
valley
leis
crops
instead
opening
island
honor
endangered

Improve Your Test Scores
1. C
2. B
3. D
4. B
5. C
6. B
7. A
8. C
9. A
10. C

Thanks, Dr. Seuss
pages 23-27

Get the Details
writing and illustrating children's books

The ABC's of Dr. Seuss
1. adored   5. right
2. illustrated 6. secret
3. publish   7. work
4. reading   8. wrote

Words Match Meanings
1. secret   5. illustrated
2. reading   6. publish
3. right   7. wrote
4. adored   8. work

Sentence Sense with Seuss
1. adored   5. work
2. illustrated 6. secret
3. wrote   7. right
4. publish   8. reading

Complete This Puzzle
1. work   4. publish
2. reading   5. adored
3. right   6. wrote
             wet pet

Test-taking Secrets Revealed
1. B   6. C
2. A   7. B
3. B   8. D
4. B   9. C
5. A   10. A

Mystery Voice Is Puzzling
pages 28-32

What's the Big Idea?
The voices you hear in cartoons sometimes belong to actors you know.

Alphabet Puts Words in Order
1. artists   5. music
2. behind   6. script
3. comic   7. star
4. heard   8. writers

Get Your Facts Right
1. writers   5. script
2. comic   6. music
3. artists   7. star
4. behind   8. heard

Words Star in Sentences
1. music   5. heard
2. artists   6. script
3. star   7. writers
4. behind   8. comic

Put Two and Two Together
1. writers   3. behind
2. heard   4. music

Secrets to Success on Tests
1. C   6. C
2. C   7. C
3. A   8. B
4. B   9. A
5. D   10. D

Children Squeal with Delight Over This Perfect Pet
pages 33-37

You've Got the Idea!
pot-bellied pigs as pets

Bring Order to These "Hog-wild" Words
1. care   5. looking
2. caves   6. pet
3. clean   7. pool
4. cool   8. written

Words Match Meanings
1. clean   5. looking
2. pet   6. cool
3. caves   7. care
4. written   8. pool

Finishing Off the Sentences
1. written   5. clean
2. pet   6. care
3. looking   7. caves
4. cool   8. pool

A Puzzling Pig Puzzle
Across
1. clean   5. pool
3. care   6. looking
Down
1. caves   4. cool
2. written   5. pet

Test-taking Secrets Revealed
1. A   3. D   5. B   7. D   9. D
2. C   4. B   6. B   8. C   10. B

Scientists Study Rocks to "Save Face!"
pages 38-42

Choose a Title
"Saving Mount Rushmore"

Alphabet Puts Words in Order
1. artist   5. giant
2. carved   6. map
3. cracks   7. sculpture
4. fix   8. sight

Words Make Meanings
1. giant   5. cracks
2. sight   6. sculpture
3. artist   7. fix
4. map   8. carved

Words Complete Sentences
1. cracks   5. map
2. artist   6. giant
3. carved   7. sight
4. sculpture   8. fix

Antonyms Are Opposites
1. giant   4. winter
2. big   5. same
3. cold   6. go

Test-day Tips Told
1. B   6. D
2. C   7. B
3. A   8. C
4. D   9. B
5. A   10. D

Visitors from Outer Space Come to Earth
pages 43-47

Questions Answered About Space Visitors
1. no
2. yes
3. no
4. yes

Be a Star with the Alphabet
1. dark
2. dust
3. light
4. night
5. rock
6. sky
7. stone
8. visitors

Words and Meanings—A Match Made in Heaven
1. visitors
2. night
3. sky
4. stone
5. light
6. rock
7. dust
8. dark

Missing Words Fall to Earth
1. visitors
2. night
3. sky
4. light
5. stone
6. rock
7. dust
8. dark

Similar Words Group Together
1. statue, building, wall
2. sun, moon, airplane
3. sun, lamp, fire

Score Higher on Tests
1. B
2. C
3. D
4. A
5. C
6. C
7. C
8. A
9. D
10. D

Caterpillar Sprouts Wings, Flies Away
pages 48-52

Cause Believed Hidden in Story
Its wings will not work yet.

Alpha-Butterflies
1. becomes
2. butterfly
3. caterpillar
4. changes
5. cocoon
6. grown
7. hangs
8. worm

Meaning Gives Words Wings
1. butterfly
2. worm
3. caterpillar
4. cocoon
5. changes
6. hangs
7. grown
8. becomes

Sentences Sprout New Words
1. worm
2. butterfly
3. caterpillar
4. cocoon
5. grown
6. hangs
7. changes
8. becomes

Words Take Flight After Mix-up
1. caterpillar
2. worm
3. butterfly
4. hangs
5. cocoon
6. grown
7. becomes
8. changes

Improve Your Score
1. D
2. A
3. B
4. C
5. B
6. C
7. A
8. C
9. A
10. D

110

Cross When Green . . . Not in Between!
pages 53-57

First Things First
He was a curious boy.

Alphabet Keeps Words in Order
1. breathe
2. curious
3. idea
4. invented
5. problems
6. safe
7. streets
8. traffic

Words and Meanings Take Shape
1. breathe
2. invented
3. traffic
4. idea
5. streets
6. curious
7. problems
8. safe

Words Fill in Sentence Holes
1. safe
2. curious
3. breathe
4. invented
5. streets
6. problems
7. traffic
8. idea

Antonyms Are Opposites
1. d
2. e
3. a
4. b
5. c
6. c
7. a
8. e
9. b
10. d

Secrets to Success on Tests
1. C
2. D
3. A
4. B
5. A
6. C
7. B
8. C
9. B
10. C

Boring Town Is a Big Hit
pages 58-62

Name the Main Idea
Some towns have strange names.

Alphabet Puts Words in Order
1. always
2. because
3. far
4. includes
5. might
6. some
7. strange
8. town

There's Hope That Words Match Meanings
1. some
2. always
3. because
4. town
5. far
6. includes
7. strange
8. might

There's Hope for Incomplete Sentences
1. some
2. always
3. because
4. town
5. far
6. includes
7. strange
8. might

Puzzle Mystery Solved
Across
1. might
4. some
5. always
7. because

Down
2. includes
3. town
4. strange
6. far

Secrets to Success on Tests
1. D
2. C
3. B
4. B
5. D
6. C
7. B
8. C
9. A
10. C

Wanted: Safety for Wildlife
pages 63-67

Placing First Things First
Hunters killed elephants and walruses.

ABC's Put Words in Order
1. crime 5. objects
2. elephants 6. remove
3. ivory 7. tusks
4. laboratory 8. walruses

Words and Meanings Match
1. remove 5. walruses
2. tusks 6. elephants
3. crime 7. ivory
4. laboratory 8. objects

Solve the Mystery of the Missing Words
1. crime 5. laboratory
2. objects 6. ivory
3. tusks 7. walruses
4. elephants 8. remove

Sound Won't Help
ate Aunt
read meet
our our

Test-taking Secrets Revealed
1. B 6. A
2. C 7. A
3. C 8. C
4. A 9. B
5. A 10. C

Dine with Devils—Meals Are a Scream!
pages 73-77

Bad-mannered Devils
on an island south of Australia

Spin Through the Alphabet
1. alone 5. scream
2. creatures 6. south
3. gobble 7. spin
4. manners 8. swallow

Words and Meanings Match
1. manners 5. spin
2. alone 6. swallow
3. gobble 7. south
4. creatures 8. scream

Words Discovered in Groups
1. dogs, cats, hamsters
2. principal, students, teacher
3. food, meat, fruit

The Final Word on Incomplete Sentences
1. alone 5. scream
2. creatures 6. south
3. manners 7. gobble
4. spin 8. swallow

Test-day Tips Told
1. B 6. B
2. C 7. A
3. A 8. D
4. C 9. B
5. C 10. A

Family Acts Up
pages 68-72

Search Is On for Details
They are challenging scenes to act.

Alphabet House Incomplete
1. child 5. millions
2. family 6. scenes
3. house 7. school
4. identical 8. twins

Words Need Meaning
1. scenes 5. identical
2. twins 6. school
3. house 7. millions
4. child 8. family

Sentence Holes Need Filling
1. scenes 5. family
2. identical 6. house
3. child 7. school
4. millions 8. twins

Find the Words in Puzzle

Score Higher on Tests
1. D 3. A 5. B 7. C 9. A
2. B 4. D 6. A 8. C 10. C

True Story About Teddy Bears
pages 78-82

What's the Cause?
He sold toy bears instead.

ABC's Put Words in Order
1. cub 5. replied
2. drawing 6. story
3. kind 7. toy
4. leader 8. trip

Words Match Up with Meanings
1. replied 5. story
2. trip 6. cub
3. kind 7. leader
4. drawing 8. toy

Fill in the Missing Words
1. toy 5. leader
2. trip 6. kind
3. replied 7. story
4. drawing 8. cub

Teddy Bears Help Solve Puzzle
Across
3. toy 6. leader
4. drawing
Down
1. story 3. trip
2. kind 5. replied

Improve Your Test Scores
1. B 6. C
2. A 7. C
3. C 8. D
4. D 9. B
5. B 10. A

Screaming Guests Throw Hands Up in Air
pages 83-87

Order the Roller Coasters
the wooden slide in Russia

Alphabet Takes Words on a Ride
1. climb
2. metal
3. park
4. slippery
5. speedy
6. thrill
7. wooden
8. zooming

Coast Through These Meanings
1. speedy
2. wooden
3. zooming
4. park
5. thrill
6. climb
7. metal
8. slippery

Coast to a Complete Sentence
1. park
2. metal
3. thrill
4. speedy
5. slippery
6. zooming
7. wooden
8. climb

Coaster Causes Scramble
1. wooden
2. park
3. metal
4. speedy
5. thrill
6. slippery
7. climb
8. zooming

Secrets to Success on Tests
1. C
2. B
3. D
4. A
5. C
6. B
7. D
8. B
9. D
10. C

Stamps Come from Far-away Lands
pages 93-97

What's the Reason?
to enjoy as a hobby

ABC's Put Words in Order
1. collect
2. hobby
3. mail
4. save
5. sort
6. stamps
7. subjects
8. wonderful

Words and Meanings Match Up
1. collect
2. mail
3. hobby
4. stamps
5. subjects
6. save
7. wonderful
8. sort

Put Your Stamp on These Sentences
1. sort
2. wonderful
3. collect
4. hobby
5. save
6. mail
7. stamps
8. subjects

The Search Is On

```
O B W J Y K M Z L
N H O B B Y E S P
X I N H M J G T A
I M D S A V E A F
C H E W I U B M E
S O R T L A G P Q
L S F R V F C S D
D S U B J E C T S
C O L L E C T E T
```

Test-taking Secrets Revealed
1. C
2. A
3. B
4. A
5. A
6. C
7. B
8. B
9. C
10. C

Medicine Cabinet Found in Backyard
pages 88-92

What's the Cause?
They want to get vitamin C.

ABC's Put Words in Order
1. backyard
2. citrus
3. drugstore
4. harvest
5. meadows
6. shortage
7. vitamin
8. wound

Words Search for Meanings
1. harvest
2. backyard
3. vitamin
4. citrus
5. drugstore
6. wound
7. meadows
8. shortage

Words Fill Sentence Holes
1. vitamin
2. backyard
3. harvest
4. wound
5. meadows
6. citrus
7. shortage
8. drugstore

Pick from Synonym Garden
lid—top
story—tale
peek—look
big—large
spin—twirl

Test Your Best
1. C
2. B
3. C
4. B
5. A
6. B
7. B
8. A
9. D
10. C

Don't Be Fooled by These Tricky Creatures
pages 98-102

Getting to the Point
It looks like a balloon with sharp points.

Keeping Words in Order
1. bottom
2. fish
3. harmless
4. mask
5. meal
6. scare
7. snake
8. tricks

No Tricks to Words and Meanings
1. mask
2. harmless
3. meal
4. snake
5. bottom
6. fish
7. scare
8. tricks

Missing Words Mask Meanings
1. fish
2. snake
3. tricks
4. harmless
5. scare
6. meal
7. mask
8. bottom

Unscrambled Letters Form New Words
1. meal
2. snake
3. scare
4. mask
5. tricks
6. bottom
7. harmless
8. fish

Score Higher on Tests
1. D
2. B
3. A
4. D
5. B
6. D
7. B
8. A
9. D
10. B